Student Companion Workbook

for use with

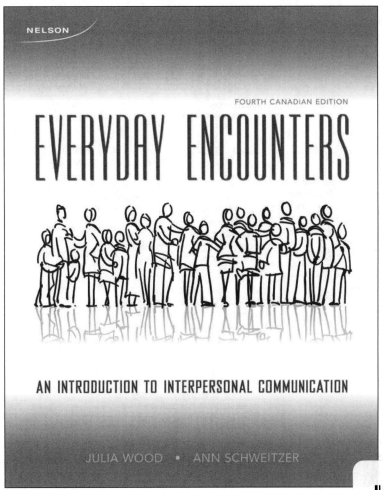

FOURTH CANADIAN EDITION

EVERYDAY ENCOUNTERS

AN INTRODUCTION TO INTERPERSONAL COMMUNICATION

JULIA WOOD • ANN SCHWEITZER

Prepared by JOANNE SPEI
HUMBER COLL

D1531175

JULIA T. WOOD
UNIVERSITY OF NORTH CAROLINA, CHAPEL HILL

and DEBI L. IBA
TEXAS CHRISTIAN UNIVERSITY

NELSON / EDUCATION

NELSON / EDUCATION

Student Companion Workbook for use with Everyday Encounters: An Introduction to Interpersonal Communication, Fourth Canadian Edition

by Joanne Spence, Julia T. Wood, and Debi L. Iba

Vice President, Editorial Director:
Evelyn Veitch

Editor-in-Chief, Higher Education:
Anne Williams

Acquisitions Editor:
Anne-Marie Taylor

Marketing Manager:
Amanda Henry

Developmental Editor:
Theresa Fitzgerald

Content Production Manager:
Christine Gilbert

Proofreader:
Cathy Witlox

Production Coordinator:
Ferial Suleman

Design Director:
Ken Phipps

Managing Designer:
Franca Amore

Printer:
RR Donnelley

ISBN-13: 978-0-17-647909-1
ISBN-10: 0-17-647909-0

Preface

Objectives of the Course and Textbook

An introductory course in interpersonal communication raises your aware of the theories and research that provide the foundations for study in this field. In addition, successfully completing a class in interpersonal communication increases communication competence in your personal and professional lives. Further, the *Everyday Encounters: An Introduction to Interpersonal Communication* textbook pays significant attention to social trends, issues, and concerns that affect how you communicate in twenty-first-century Western culture. These trends include cultural diversity, communication technologies, and timely social issues such as workplace communication, long-distance friendships, safe-sex practices in an era of HIV/AIDS, and violence between intimates.

Objectives and Format of this Student Companion

The Student Companion Workbook facilitates your understanding of the theories, concepts, and research discussed in the textbook, and provides you with an opportunity to put these ideas into practice. To make this companion user-friendly and beneficial to you, we have included the following sections in each chapter to correspond to the textbook chapters.

Chapter Content—This outline framework highlights the information contained in each textbook chapter. It asks you to complete sections of the outline in your own words and also to generate personal examples to illustrate the concepts. After reading the textbook chapter, close the textbook and see how much of the outline you can complete (this is a good way to test your initial comprehension of the material). We have found in our teaching that students are very good at memorizing the examples or definitions provided in the textbook, but if we ask the question in a different way or ask them to apply the material to a different type of situation, they are unsure at best and lost at worst. Having your own examples should help you determine how well you understand/comprehend the material and aid your ability to use this information in your relationships once you leave this classroom.

Activities—There are a number of activities that fortify and extend the textbook's coverage. Some of the activities invite you to reflect on your own experiences as a communicator while others provide you with ways of developing greater skills in communicating with and analyzing the communication of others. All activities are broken down into individual, partner, group, ethnographic (that is, where you go to participate or observe a situation and/or interview people), and Internet or InfoTrac. A grid at the beginning of each Activity section groups each exercise into these categories. Further, all the activities are printed on perforated pages so you can remove them for easy carrying and/or turning in as class assignments.

Have a wonderful interpersonal communication experience.

Table of Contents

Chapter 1: Exploring Interpersonal Communication

I.   Communication meets many of the basic human needs that Abraham Maslow identified.

      A.   Physical needs help us survive. An example of a time when I used communication to achieve this need is _____

_____

      B.   Safety needs protect us from harm. An example of a time when I used communication to meet this need is _____

_____

      C.   Belonging needs connect us to others. An example of a time when I used communication to meet this need is _____

_____

      D.   Self-esteem needs indicate that we are valued by/important to others. An example of a time when I used communication to meet this need is _____

_____

      E.   Self-actualization needs are experiences that help us reach our fullest individual potential. An example of a time when I used communication to achieve this need is _____

_____

_____

II.   Interpersonal communication is not defined by the number of people in the interaction or the context in which the communication occurs.

      A.   Models help us understand the historical roots from which our current views of communication grew.

            1.   <u>Linear models</u> treated communication as a one-way process in which one person transmitted a message to another person.

                  a.   Laswell's model answered the following five questions:

i._____

ii._____

iii._____

iv._____

v._____

                  b.   Shannon and Weaver's model illustrated how a message goes from a source to a destination and added the feature of noise. Draw a picture of their telephone model here:

                  c.   Two problems with these linear models were that they:

i._____

ii._____

2.   Interactive models addressed the weakness in linear models, which viewed listeners as passive recipients, by adding feedback to the communication process.

      a.   The interactive model recognized that communicators are both creators and interpreters of messages. The creation and interpretation processes are based upon a person's field of experience. Draw a picture of the model here:

      b.   Even with this advance, two linear model problems remained:
           i._____
           ii._____

3.   Transactional models recognize the dynamic (changing) nature of communication. Draw a picture of the transactional model here:

B.   There are three levels of communication.

      1.   <u>I–It communication</u> occurs when we treat others like objects or nonhumans. An example of a time when I used I–It communication is_____

_____

      2.   <u>I–You communication</u> occurs when we recognize the other as a person and treat him or her based upon a social role he or she occupies. This constitutes the majority of our communication. An example of a time when I engaged in I–You communication is _____

_____

      3.   <u>I–Thou communication</u> occurs when we recognize and understand an individual's unique characteristics as well as open ourselves completely to this person. An example of a time when I engaged in I–Thou communication is _____

_____

C.   Interpersonal communication is a selective, systemic, unique, and ongoing process of interaction between individuals who reflect and build personal knowledge of one another and create shared meanings.

      1.   Interpersonal communication occurs within a variety of systems and contexts.

            a.   The situation, time, people, culture, and personal histories all affect the way we create and interpret messages.

            b.   Noise is anything that distracts our attention so that we fail to give our undivided attention to an interaction. An example of physical noise that distracted me today is _____

_____

            c.   An example of psychological noise that distracted me today is_____

_____

_____

        d.   An example of semantic noise that distracted me today is _____

_____

_____

        e.   An example of physiological noise that distracted me today is_____

_____

_____

2.   Each new relationship we build is different from all of the ones that came before it. No two interpersonal relationships are exactly alike.

3.   Interpersonal communication evolves over time, is affected by our past, and influences our future.

4.   Because interpersonal communication is an interaction, both parties create and interpret messages, are responsible for the communication's effectiveness, and must get to know each other personally.

5.   Attaching meanings to the words we exchange requires knowledge of the other person and the relationship in which we are engaged.

        a.   <u>Content meanings</u> are the definitions we could look up in a dictionary. A content meaning for "You're bad" would be _____

_____

_____

        b.   <u>Relational meanings</u> are the understandings we have because of the connection we have to the other person/people involved in the interaction. A relational meaning for "You're bad" might be

_____

_____

III.   Our definition of interpersonal communication implies basic principles.

    A.   We cannot avoid communicating when we are with other people.

    B.   Because communication is irreversible, we can never take back what we say or do, and we always have an impact on the person/people with whom we are interacting.

    C.   Because interpersonal communication affects us and others, ethical considerations are always parts of our interactions. Ethical issues concern what is right and what is wrong in our interactions with others. An example of a time when I made an ethical choice in my communication is _____

_____

_____

    D.   Meanings are not in words or actions alone but rather in the participants' interpretations of those words and actions.

    E.   Metacommunication is how we let others know, both verbally and nonverbally, about whether the way we are interacting is helping us create shared understanding. It also helps us express how we feel about our interactions with our friends and/or partners.

    F.   Interpersonal communication is the primary way we build, refine, and transform relationships. A time when I constructed a shared future with a friend or intimate is

_____

_____

    G.   Interpersonal communication does not solve all problems. An example of a problem in my life that communication could not solve is _____

_____

_____

    H.   We can learn to be more competent interpersonal communicators.

IV.   Communication competence involves being both _____

and _____

      A.   Because no one style of communication works well in all situations, we must learn a variety of behaviours and know when each set of behaviours is most appropriate.

      B.   When individuals appropriately adapt their communication, they are sensitive to goals, contexts, and other people. An example of when I was sensitive to the needs of someone else and adapted my communication is _____

_____

      C.   By engaging in dual perspective, we can see not only our view of the interaction but also the other person's view of self, the situation, and thoughts or feelings in an ethical manner. This involves considering the moral implications of what we say and do, as well as how this affects others.

      D.   Monitoring our communication involves observing and regulating how we communicate with others both before and during our interactions. One time that I monitored my communication with others was _____

_____

      E.   We must be willing to commit the time and energy necessary to practice effective and ethical interpersonal communication in our relationships.

Activities

Title	Individual	Partner	Group	Ethno	Internet InfoTrac
1.1 Identifying Human Needs	✓	✓			
1.2 Recognizing the Unique Aspects of Interpersonal Communication	✓	✓	✓		
1.3 Understanding Models of Communication	✓	✓	✓	✓	
1.4 Recognizing Dimensions of Relational Level Meanings	✓				
1.5 Understanding How Technology Affects Communication Patterns	✓	✓	✓	✓	✓

Activity 1.1 Identifying Human Needs

Purpose: To increase understanding of how human needs are met in everyday life.

Instructions
1. This activity can be done individually, with a partner, or with a larger study group or class.
2. Review the case study below.
3. Identify how Imran's human needs are met in his everyday experiences.

Example
Physiological Needs: Imran goes to work every day and receives a paycheque for the work that he does. This paycheque allows him to meet many of his basic needs, such as food and housing.

Case Study
Imran works as a social worker in an employment resource centre. His job is to assist clients who come to the centre to find employment. He finds his job enjoyable and looks forward to going to work every day. He has a good network of peers who he works with and they regularly go out for lunch together and celebrate significant occasions in each other's lives. Recently, he was approached by his supervisor about the possibility of a promotion at the agency. The new position would involve examining how the agency could more effectively meet the needs of new Canadians. As a first-generation Canadian from India, he is excited about the opportunity to work with people from many different cultures. It would be something that he has never done, and Imran feels good about the fact that his supervisor thinks so highly of him. He talked to his partner at length about the opportunity as he wondered whether he was capable of handling the responsibilities associated with the new job. His partner helped him to realize that he would be able to manage it well.

Identify how Imran has his human needs met.

➤ Physiological

➤ Safety

➢   Belonging

➢   Self-Esteem

➢   Cognitive

➢   Aesthetic

➢   Self-Actualization/Self-Transcendence

➢   Peak Experiences

Activity 1.2 Recognizing the Unique Aspects of Interpersonal Communication

Purpose: To gain an understanding of the range of relationships that we have in our lives and how they change over time.

Instructions

1.   This activity can be done individually, with a partner, or with a larger study group or class.

2.   Make a list of different people you encounter on a regular basis. Make sure to include all of the different people you see and encounter, such as bus drivers, teachers, family members, and so on.

3.   Classify these relationships according to whether they are I–It, I–You, or I–Thou relationships.

4.   Pick one relationship from the I–Thou category and explain how it moved along the communication continuum from an I–It to an I–Thou relationship. How is your communication different now than when you first met?

Example

One of my best friends is Emily. I sat beside Emily at the school orientation on the first day of classes. We shook hands and introduced ourselves to each other as instructed by the facilitator. We didn't say anything more to each other until the next week when I saw her sitting by herself in the first class of the day. I sat beside her as she was a familiar face in an ocean of unfamiliar faces. Week after week, Emily and I sat together in class. Slowly we started to share more information with each other as we took our breaks together and sometimes went to the library together after class. One day she asked me if I wanted to go to the movies with her that weekend. We met for dinner beforehand and never made it to the movie. Instead, we spent the whole night talking about our lives.

The relationship with Emily was first an I–It relationship as I did not know her and we simply sat beside each other in the orientation. Over a period of weeks, the relationship moved toward an I–You relationship as we started to share more information with each other. After we spent the evening talking, our relationship moved to an I–Thou relationship, and she is now one of my best friends.

List 10 people you encounter on a daily basis:

1.
2.
3.
4.
5.

6.
7.
8.
9.
10.

What type of relationship do you have with each of these people? (I–It, I–You, I–Thou)

1.
2.
3.
4.
5.
6.
7.
8.
9.
10.

How did your I–Thou relationships evolve to become that type of relationship?

1.

2.

3.

4.

5.

6.

7.

8.

9.

10.

Activity 1.3 Understanding Models of Communication

Purpose: To increase awareness of the complexities of interpersonal communication.

Instructions

1. This activity can be done individually, with a partner, or with a larger study group or class.
2. Pick a favourite television show to observe.
3. Look at the patterns of communication that take place between the characters and answer the questions listed below.

Example

As you observe a favourite sitcom, you see that characters communicate to each other continually and often simultaneously. You may notice that one character is preoccupied with a problem that interferes with his or her ability to stay focused on the conversation. What do you notice about how the characters talk with each other and share their experiences? What miscommunication do you see, and what factors contribute to this?

Questions to Consider

Who is doing most of the talking?

How is the other person communicating simultaneously?

Do they take turns talking or communicating?

How does culture affect the way they are talking?

Are you aware of any of the characters experiencing physiological noise? How is this affecting the communication?

What type of physical noise is present in the situation that you are observing?

What type of psychological noise is interfering with the communication between the characters?

Are there examples of semantic noise? Is this unique to you because of your culture or other factors that might be present?

Activity 1.4 Recognizing Dimensions of Relational Level Meanings

Purpose: To increase your awareness of relational level meanings in interpersonal communication.

Instructions

Recall that relational level meanings have three dimensions: liking, responsiveness, and control. In each of the following examples of communication, identify which dimension of relational level meaning seems to predominate.

1.   When Frances's parents criticize her for not coming home more often from school, she responds by saying, "Look, I'm 20 years old, and you can't expect me to be at home every weekend."

Dimension of relational communication: _____

2.   Edwin says to his five-year-old daughter, "You clean up your room right now."

Dimension of relational communication: _____

3.   Adrienne asks her friend Malcolm if he wants to come over for dinner and conversation.

Dimension of relational communication: _____

4.   Jerry tells his friend Michael about a personal problem, and Michael doesn't respond. Jerry then says, "Hey, am I invisible or something?"

Dimension of relational communication: _____

5.   Alfonso says to his partner, "I think you are the greatest person in the world."

Dimension of relational communication: _____

6.   As Kim talks, Pat nods her head and smiles to show that she is following and interested in what Kim says.

Dimension of relational communication: _____

Activity 1.5 Understanding How Technology Affects Communication Patterns

Purpose: To gain an awareness of how people communicate relational level meaning to others while using electronic communication devices such as social web pages, chat rooms, and cellphones.

Instructions

1.   This activity can be done individually, with a partner, or with a larger study group or class.
2.   Go to a social web page such as Facebook and engage in a "chat" with someone online.
3.   If working in a group, determine a time that all group members can be online to chat simultaneously.
4.   As you are chatting, observe how people communicate with each other when they do not see each other face to face.
5.   Upon completion of the activity, answer the debriefing questions below.
6.   These questions can be posted for discussion on the chat site to continue the exercise.

Example

All of your classmates decide that they are going to go online to discuss the concepts from the class. While you participate, you become aware of how people signal to each other that they want to speak. You also notice how people communicate relational level meaning to each other through the use of certain expressions and emoticons. You start to notice how this is similar or different from face-to-face communication.

Debriefing Questions

How do people signal that they want to speak when online?

What happens when multiple people speak online?

Do you notice any miscommunication between people?

How do you communicate your emotions to each other?

If there are people from different cultures within your group, ask them to comment on any differences that they notice when they use chat rooms with people from their culture or language.

How is the communication different when you speak online from when you speak face to face?

Chapter 2: Communication and the Creation of Self

I. The self is a complicated, multidimensional process.

    A. We develop notions of who we are and aren't because of our interactions with others from the time we are born until the time we die.

        1. We develop images of ourselves, both positive and negative, based upon the messages others communicate to us.

            a. An example of a positive <u>self-fulfilling prophecy</u> is

_____

_____

_____

            b. An example of a negative <u>self-fulfilling prophecy</u> is

_____

_____

_____

        2. Communication with three different groups of people is most influential in helping us develop our self.

            a. Family members are usually the first to influence our development of the self.

                i. Family members provide <u>direct definitions</u> by labelling our behaviours and us. An example of a direct definition my family provided for me is _____

_____

                ii. Family members also provide <u>identity scripts</u> that define our roles, how we play them, and the general progression of our life. An example of an identity script in my family is _____

_____

        iii.   Parents or primary caregivers communicate who we are by how they interact with us, or their <u>attachment styles</u>. In my family, we had a(n) _____ attachment style because we interacted with each other by _____

        _____

    b.   Early in life we begin to interact with our peers, who also help us figure out who we are.

        i.   <u>Reflected appraisals</u> indicate who our peers believe us to be as well as what behaviours are appropriate or inappropriate in these interactions. An example of a reflected appraisal from my life is_____

        _____

        ii.   We also compare ourselves with those around us. An example of a <u>social comparison</u> in which I engaged recently is _____

        _____

    c.   Society as a whole also influences how we see our behaviour and ourselves.

        i.   The <u>generalized other</u> reflects the views that others in a society generally hold.

        ii.   Perspectives of the generalized other are communicated through the media, institutions, and individuals who reflect or have internalized cultural values.

B.   There are many different ways we view our selves, including physical, emotional, social, and moral.

C.   Because it involves a process, the self develops over the course of time.

1.   Ego boundaries define where an individual stops and the world begins.

2.   Development of the self is a continuous process.

D.   Two kinds of social perspectives help us define our self because we learn what society values and generally develop a shared sense of what is important to thrive.

1.   <u>Particular others</u> are specific individuals who we consider significant in our lives and who show how they see us. Particular others in my life include _____

_____

2.   The <u>generalized other</u> is a collection of rules, roles, and attitudes accepted as appropriate by the social community in which we live.

a.   Race, gender, sexual orientation, and socioeconomic class are prevalent identifiers in Western culture.

b.   The generalized other unequally values different races, genders, socioeconomic classes, and sexual orientations.

E.   Because social perspectives are defined in a particular time and place, they are open to revision as our situations change.

II.   There are four guidelines for strengthening our self or view of our identity.

A.   We must make a commitment to finding ways to help us grow. An example of a way that I can help myself grow is _____

_____

B.   Once we are committed, it is important to understand how our self has developed as well as what changes are desirable and how to help them happen. An example of a change I would like to make is _____

I can aid in the process by _____

_____.

C.   Rather than setting ourselves up for failure by attempting to make radical changes in our self, we need to set realistic goals with realistic standards.

D.   We need to choose settings that and people who will help us achieve our goals.

1.   Uppers are people who communicate positively about us and reflect positive appraisals of our value as individuals. Someone who can serve as an upper in helping me achieve my goal is _____

_____.

2.   Downers are people who communicate negatively about us and reflect negative appraisals of our value as individuals. Someone who would keep me from achieving my goal is _____

_____.

3.   Vultures are extreme versions of downers. They communicate negatively about us by attacking our view of self. Someone who would sabotage my attempt to reach my goal is _____

_____.

4.   Self-sabotage occurs when we act as a downer or vulture for ourselves. One way I am going to avoid self-sabotage is _____

_____.

Activities

Title	Individual	Partner	Group	Ethno	Internet InfoTrac
2.1 Recognizing Influences on the Sense of Self	✓	✓	✓	✓	✓
2.2 Identifying Your Identity Scripts	✓	✓	✓	✓	✓
2.3 My Personal Web Page	✓	✓	✓	✓	✓
2.4 Recognizing the Communication of Uppers, Downers, and Vultures	✓	✓			
2.5 Your Many Windows	✓	✓			

Activity 2.1 Recognizing Influences on the Sense of Self

Purpose: To identify factors that influence the sense of self.

Instructions
1. This activity can be done individually, with a partner, or with a larger study group or class, or be posted online for analysis and discussion.
2. Read the continued case study of Imran below.
3. Answer the questions below with regards to the concept of the influence on the sense of self.

Case Study
As Imran was taking the bus home from work, he started to think about how lucky he was to be offered the promotion. He thought about his friend Sasha, who had worked there just as long as he had but did not seem to have the same opportunities offered to him. Imran wondered whether it was because Sasha was often distant from people and never took the time to go for lunch or to socialize with colleagues. He knew that it was hard for Sasha as he was very shy and avoided friendships. He had once confided to Imran that his parents were very abusive while he was growing up and that he did not trust people. Imran wonders if that situation has affected Sasha's self-confidence. Imran feels lucky when he compares Sasha's background to his own upbringing with two very loving parents. He thinks about how often they told him he was smart and how much they believed in him. They always told him that he could be anything he wanted to be if he put his mind to it.

What factors influenced Sasha's sense of self?

How has this influenced him?

What factors influenced Imran's sense of self?

How has this influenced him?

Where do you see an example of social comparison? How do you think that this influences what Imran thinks of himself?

Do you see any examples of the concept of self-fulfilling prophecy? What do you think the impact was?

Activity 2.2 Identifying Your Identity Scripts

Purpose: To help you recognize identity scripts communicated to you by members of your family. To help you understand the differences between identity scripts from culture to culture.

Instructions

1.   This activity can be done individually, with a partner, or with a larger study group or class, or be posted online for analysis and discussion.
2.   Complete each sentence below by filling in what members of your family told you when you were a child. Put a checkmark by each of the scripts that you still live by.
3.   Review the scripts you no longer use. How or why did you decide to abandon these scripts?
4.   Compare your results with those of a partner or of a group that includes individuals from a different culture.
5.   How do the scripts differ? How are they the same?

Example

Money is to be saved.

I no longer live by this script. I chose to give it up after my best friend was hit by a car and killed. I decided then that life is too short and that I was going to live for the moment, which means spending my money how and when I want. Why bother saving?

Money is …

Nobody in our family has ever ...

You can/cannot (pick one) trust others.

The most important goal in life is ...

Good people ...

You can't trust people who ...

Families should ...

If you want others to respect you, you should ...

Activity 2.3 My Personal Web Page

Purpose: To become aware of what people communicate about themselves through their personal web pages.

Instructions

1.   This activity can be done individually, with a partner, or with a larger study group or class, or be posted online for analysis and discussion.

2.   Visit five personal web pages.
   - ➢   Your own
   - ➢   That of a friend
   - ➢   That of an older family member
   - ➢   That of a person from a culture different from your own
   - ➢   That of a business

3.   Make a list of the type of information that each person puts on his or her home page.

4.   Answer the question below in order to compare and analyze the pages.

Example

You may notice that all of your friends tend to have the same type of information, pictures, and graphics on their personal web pages. You may see that the choice of information posted reflects the value system of the people. What have you learned about them and how they define themselves?

Questions to Reflect On

What type of information appeared the most frequently?

What type of information was not included?

Are there any patterns relating to what was posted and what wasn't?

How do you think the web pages represent the values of the person who or organization that posted the site? In what way?

Did you notice any significant difference between the web pages of the individuals who were older or of a different gender or culture?

Discuss your insights with a partner or with your class and compare your responses.

How were their responses different from your own?

Activity 2.4 Recognizing the Communication of Uppers, Downers, and Vultures

Purpose: To increase your awareness of the communication styles of people who are uppers, downers, and vultures and of their impact on your self-concept.

Instructions

1.   This activity can be done individually or with a partner.
2.   Identify three people with whom you interact:
   a.   One person you have a very positive relationship with and you feel good about yourself with—an upper.
   b.   One person who often leaves you feeling upset after you've spent time together—a downer.
   c.   One person you always feel vulnerable with and you feel you cannot trust—a vulture.
3.   Write the names of the three people in the three blanks at the left of the form below.
4.   Beside each name describe specific verbal and nonverbal communication that the person uses to enact the role of upper, downer, or vulture.
5.   How do you feel after the person communicates to you in this manner?
6.   Are you aware of how you respond to this person? If so, what are the differences?

Example

You notice that every time you get together with Marla you feel sad afterward. You decide to look more closely at the communication patterns. You note that she often cuts you off in the middle of your sentences. As well, she monopolizes the conversation, leaving you without a chance to talk about things that are on your mind. Further, you recall that she often answers her cellphone in the middle of your conversations and you end up sitting there while she talks with someone else. You feel left out and frustrated that she does not think you are important enough to focus on right now.

Role/Person	Verbal Communication	Nonverbal Communication	How Do I Feel Afterward?

Activity 2.5 Your Many Windows

Purpose: To allow you to apply the Johari Window to your life to discover the content in the different windows of yourself. To increase awareness of the differences in what you communicate about yourself to others and what you know about yourself.

Instructions

1. On the following pages you will find three copies of blank Johari Windows—one each for a parent, your best friend, and a past or current romantic partner.
2. Fill in each Johari Window by writing information about you that fits each pane in the window for that particular relationship.
3. When you have filled in all three Johari Windows, compare the kinds of information that fits in each pane among the different relationships.
4. Ask each of these people to complete the Johari Window exercise in order to give you feedback on the Blind Window of the exercise.
5. Compare the kinds of information that you have put into the different panes for each of the relationships.
6. What did you learn about yourself from the feedback you received from the people who completed the Johari Window exercise?

Example

You may notice that there are things you communicate to your partner that you don't communicate to your parent. Your partner and your parent may have different feedback to give you about what they see about you. How has this changed in the course of your relationship with these people?

Relationship 1: With a parent (either parent)

	Known to Self	Unknown to Self
K n o w n t o O t h e r s	Open Area	Blind Area
U n k n o w n t o O t h e r s	Hidden Area	Unknown Area

Relationship 2: With your best friend

	Known to Self	Unknown to Self
K n o w n t o O t h e r s	Open Area	Blind Area
U n k n o w n t o O t h e r s	Hidden Area	Unknown Area

Relationship 3: With a current or former romantic partner

	Known to Self	Unknown to Self
Known to Others	Open Area	Blind Area
Unknown to Others	Hidden Area	Unknown Area

Chapter 3: Perception and Communication

I. Perception is an active process of creating meaning by selecting, organizing, and interpreting people, objects, events, situations, and activities. Essentially, how do we make sense of what happens in the world around us?

    A. We consciously select which of the infinite number of stimuli around us is most relevant at any point in time. Stop what you are doing for a moment and write down one example of

        something you see: _____;

        something you smell: _____;

        something you hear: _____;

        something you feel: _____;

        and something going on inside your body: _____.

        1. We select stimuli that stand out above the others. _____ _____ is the stimulus that stood out most in my list above.

        2. We influence what we select by noticing things we had not noticed before. In class today, one thing I noticed that I had not noticed before was _____ _____.

        3. Who we are, what we need, why we need it, and where we are at a moment in time influence what we select. In class, I am most tuned in to_____ _____.

        because _____.

        4. The culture in which we grow up and live also influences what we select to perceive. Because I grew up in _____, I am more likely to notice _____ _____.

B.   We use four organizational structures (schemata) to make sense of what we have selected
      to notice.

    1.   Prototypes represent the most typical or ideal example of a particular group of
      people, places, objects, activities, relationships, or events. A <u>prototype</u> for

      _____ is

      _____.

    2.   Personal constructs are bipolar dimensions of judgment we use to determine
      where someone or something fits. When I meet someone new, the <u>personal</u>
      <u>constructs</u> I use to judge that person are _____.

    3.   Stereotypes are generalizations that we perceive represent a majority, but not all,
      of the people or things in a particular category. Stereotypes allow us to create a
      set of expected behaviours. An example of a <u>stereotype</u> that I have for

      _____is

      _____.

    4.   Scripts are a sequence of behaviours that we have for how we and others should
      act in particular situations. An example of a <u>script</u> we use in my family is _____

      _____.

C.   Interpretation is the process of attaching meaning or explanations to what we have
      noticed and organized.

    1.   Attributions are explanations for why things happen or people act the way they
      do. An example of an <u>attribution</u> I made yesterday was _____

      _____.

    2.   Attribution errors occur when we attach distorted meanings to what
      happens around us.

        a.   A self-serving bias occurs when we take excessive personal credit for our
      successes or assume someone or something else is responsible for our poor

performances. An example of a time when I committed the <u>self-serving bias</u> is _____

_____ .

    b.   A fundamental attribution error occurs when we overestimate the internal causes and underestimate the external causes of others' undesirable behaviours or when we overestimate the external causes and underestimate the internal causes of our undesirable behaviours. An example of a time when I committed the <u>fundamental attribution error</u> is_____

_____ .

II.   At least six factors affect our perception process.

    A.   Human physiology indicates that not everyone's five senses, biorhythms, or medical conditions are exactly the same. An example of how human physiology affected my perception today is _____

_____ .

    B.   Age and the number of experiences accompanying it alter our view or interpretation of particular communication situations. One of the things that I perceive differently than do people in the generation before me is _____

_____ .

    C.   Our culture leads each of us to have a particular set of beliefs, values, understandings, and practices that influence our perception process. Because of my culture, today I perceived _____
differently than someone in another culture would.

    D.   Our various standpoints, or social groups to which we belong in a particular culture, shape our point of view. An example of a time my standpoint shaped how I perceived a person or situation was _____

_____ .

E.   How we are taught to enact social roles and the behaviours we actually perform to carry out our social roles influence how we perceive the world around us. An example of a time when my social role influenced my perception of a person or behaviour is _____

_____

_____.

F.   Cognitive abilities indicate the number of different interpretations we can create for a situation.

1.   People who have more schemata for organizing and interpreting situations are considered more cognitively complex.

2.   When using person-centred communication, we interact with an individual as a unique human being. An example of a time when I used person-centred communication is _____

_____.

3.   We empathize with another when we do our best to feel what another person is feeling in a particular situation. A recent experience in which I used empathy is

_____.

G.   Our selves also influence how we select, organize, and interpret stimuli.

1.   Attachment styles influence how we perceive others, situations, and messages. An example of when my attachment style influenced how I perceived someone else is_____

_____.

2.   We have implicit personality theories of interaction characteristics that we believe go together. An example of a time when I used the implicit personality theory is _____

_____.

III.   There are many ways we can improve the accuracy of our perceptions.

A.   We need to understand that all of our perceptions occur at a point in time, represent only a portion of the stimuli we could notice, and cannot be determined to be true or false. An example of a time when I should have noticed that perceptions are static, partial, and unverifiable is _____.

B.   We need to avoid assuming that we know what another person thinks or how she or he perceives a particular situation. An example of a time when I should have avoided assuming is _____.

C.   Perception checking occurs when we ask others to check the extent to which our perceptions are accurate so that we can create a shared understanding of each other, the situation, and our relationship. An example of a time when I should have engaged in perception checking is _____.

D.   We need to recognize the difference between facts (those things we can verify based on observation) and inferences (those things we create by interpreting what we have observed). An example of a time when I should not have confused facts and inferences is

_____.

E.   We need to guard against self-serving bias because it can distort our perceptions. An example of a time when the self-serving bias distorted my perceptions is _____

_____.

F.   We can avoid the fundamental attribution error by looking for external reasons for others' actions and internal motivations for our own. An example of a time when I should have guarded against the fundamental attribution error is _____

_____.

G.   We need to remember that the label we attach to a particular interaction affects not only how we perceive that situation, but also how we will behave in future interactions. An example of a time when I should have paid more attention to labels is _____

_____.

Activities

Title	Individual	Partner	Group	Ethno	Internet InfoTrac
3.1 Applying Cognitive Schemata	✓	✓	✓	✓	
3.2 Checking Your Assumptions	✓	✓	✓	✓	
3.3 Influences on Your Perception			✓	✓	
3.4 Remaking the Social World			✓		
3.5 Look at What You See		✓	✓	✓	✓

Activity 3.1 Applying Cognitive Schemata

Purpose: To practise actively using cognitive schemata as a perception tool.

Instructions

1. This activity can be done individually, with a partner, or with a larger study group or class.
2. Review the case study of Imran presented below.
3. After you have read the story, answer the questions provided.
4. Discuss your answers with your partner or study group.
5. How were your answers the same or different?
6. If your answers were different, why do you think this is?

Case Study

Imran can't stop thinking about the possibility of the promotion. He really likes Althea, the woman who would become his supervisor, and knows that she has done a great deal to promote his skills to the management of the agency. He starts to think back on the other supervisors he has had, including former teachers, and thinks about what makes a good supervisor. Imran thinks that the best supervisor he ever had was his cricket coach in high school. This man was fabulous because he would call his students by name, make a point of checking in on them, and use encouragement as a way of motivating them. Imran also thinks about the worst boss he ever had. She was a very pushy woman who looked out for only the people she liked. He knows that Althea is from the same culture as this previous supervisor, and he wonders whether she will end up being the same way with him eventually. He starts to feel nervous, wondering if he is making the right choice in considering this job. What if Althea turns out to be a horrible boss just like the other woman he worked for?

Questions

Identify how Imran used schemata to organize his thinking about his supervisor.

Based on what you know, what is the prototype that Imran uses to measure his supervisor?

What are the personal constructs that he has used to measure supervisors as good or bad?

What is his stereotype of a good supervisor?

What scripts does Imran carry in his head about supervisors?

How might these scripts affect his perception?

Activity 3.2 Checking Your Assumptions

Purpose: To further your understanding of the attribution errors that we make.

Instructions

    1.   This activity can be done individually, with a partner, or with a larger study group or class. It can also be posted online for a distance study group.

    2.   Read the story below.

    3.   Make a list of the assumptions that the teacher made about the student.

    4.   Make a list of the attribution errors you see.

    5.   Are any of the errors a self-serving bias?

    6.   What could be done to avoid the assumptions?

Example

If a friend of yours is late for dinner, you may assume that she is selfish for not being considerate of the time you are wasting while you wait for her. You later find out that she had a car accident on the way to see you and is now in the hospital. This is an example of an attribution error. You assumed she was being thoughtless when in fact she was simply not able to call you because she had been hospitalized.

Story

A teacher is in her classroom waiting to start her 10:00 sociology class. At 10:15, a student by the name of Marcia walks into the class and sits down very noisily in her seat. The teacher feels aggravated. Marcia is late for her class every day. Her constant lateness and her disruption to the class when she comes in leads the teacher to believe that Marcia is not very committed to the course. Once Marcia sits down, she pulls out her cellphone and starts to type on the keyboard. The teacher feels more frustration as she thinks that this is a further demonstration of Marcia's lack of commitment. The teacher takes note of other behaviours that Marcia engages in, such as looking at her watch and frequently glancing out of the window.

Questions

What facts do you know about this story?

What assumptions might you make about both characters?

What attribution errors are you aware of?

Are there any examples of a self-serving bias?

What could the parties do to avoid making attribution errors?

Activity 3.3 Influences on Your Perception

Purpose: To increase your awareness of factors that influence your perception.

Instructions
1. Complete this activity with a group of people.
2. Pick a sitcom or popular television show to view.
3. Choose one character to focus on during the show.
4. Provide each person in your group with a list of factors to watch for during the show.
5. Compare and discuss your different opinions about the character.
6. Note what factors influenced what you saw in the character.

Example
You decide that you are going to watch a drama as a group. As you watch the show and observe one of the main characters, you notice that he is very abrupt with his colleagues and that you feel angry toward him. You mention these thoughts to your group, and some members state that they found the character's behaviour funny and did not see anything insulting. You discuss the differences in how you view the same behaviours.

Behaviours to Observe

Do you like the character?

What aspects of the character's personality do you like?

What aspects of the character's personality do you not like?

How does the character behave toward others with whom he or she interacts?

What factors have influenced your opinion?

- Physiology

- Age

- Culture

- Role

- Cognitive Ability

- Self

Activity 3.4 Remaking the Social World

Purpose: To enhance your awareness of the arbitrariness and the impact of categories that societies use to define people. To allow you to imagine how society would be different if different categories for defining people were used.

Instructions
1. Join with 5 or 6 other people in your class to form a discussion group.
2. As a group, devise a method of classifying people. You may not use race, class, sex, or sexual orientation to classify individuals.
3. Suggest some of the implications of the classifications you devise.
4. After 20 minutes of group discussion, make a report to the class in which you do the following:

   a. Describe your system of classifying people.

   b. Provide a rationale for the method of classification you chose.

   c. Explain some of the political, economic, educational, and social consequences that would be likely if people were classified, and thus perceived, only with reference to your system.

Activity 3.5 Look at What You See

Purpose: To increase your awareness of how you see things differently from others based upon what you look for.

Instructions

1. This activity can be done with a partner or with a larger study group or class. It can also be posted online for a distance study group.
2. On the Internet, perform a search for "visual perception images."
3. Choose five images to look at.
4. Examine each, listing what you see.
5. Compare your perspectives with those of your partner or group members.
6. Discuss how you selected what to pay attention to in the image.
7. What other factors, such as gender or culture, affected what you looked at?

Example

There are many examples of images that challenge our visual perception. We see things a certain way and can find it hard to look at things differently. Each of us is unique and has a different lens through which we view the same image. In order to understand why we see things differently, we must learn the factors that influence others' perceptions.

Chapter 4: Emotions and Communication

I.   How well we communicate emotions influences the depth and quality of our interpersonal relationships.

   A.   Emotional intelligence is being able to recognize and communicate the feelings appropriate and necessary for a given situation or context. A person I know who has a high <u>emotional intelligence</u> is _____; recently, this person exhibited emotional intelligence when he or she _____ _____.

   B.   <u>Emotions</u> occur over time because physiology, perceptions, and social experiences influence them.

      1.   A physiological approach to emotion, also known as the <u>organismic view of emotions</u>, suggests that we experience a stimulus that creates a physiological reaction so that we can then experience an emotion. Currently, this view is not widely accepted.

      2.   A <u>perceptual view of emotions</u> suggests that we experience a stimulus that creates our perception of the event and interpretation of the emotion so that we can have a physiological response.

      3.   A <u>cognitive labelling view of emotions</u> suggests that we experience a stimulus that creates a physiological response to which we attach a label so that we can experience an emotion.

      4.   An <u>interactive view of emotions</u> suggests that what we feel and how we express those feelings is intricately tied to our social situation.

         a.   <u>Framing rules</u> are guidelines for defining the emotional meaning of situations. For me, the framing rules associated with high school graduation are _____.

         b.   <u>Feeling rules</u> tell us what we should feel or expect to feel in particular situations based upon our society's values. For me, the feeling rules associated with high school graduation are _____ _____.

C. Emotion work is the time and energy we need to put forth to generate what we believe is a desired outcome in a particular situation. A recent time I engaged in emotion work is _____

_____ .

D. The approach we adopt toward emotions affects our belief that we can (or can't) control our emotions and the feelings we can experience and express in our everyday lives.

II. There are two related sets of obstacles to effective emotional communication.

A. Just because we feel an emotion does not mean we express it to others.

1. Social expectations for Westerners indicate that it is more acceptable for women to express emotions and for men to refrain from expressing most emotions. An example of when I based my choice to express or not express emotions on social expectations is _____

_____ .

2. Exposing our emotions to others makes us vulnerable because we do not necessarily know how our disclosures may be used in future interactions. An example of a time when I based my choice to express or not express emotions on vulnerability is _____

_____ .

3. In an effort to protect those we care about, we sometimes choose not to express our emotions. An example of a time when I based my choice to express or not express emotions on protecting others is

_____

_____ .

4. Certain social and professional roles dictate that we not express certain types of emotions.

B.   Just because we express an emotion does not mean that we communicate it effectively.

   1.   Abstract statements of feelings do not indicate how we truly feel in a given situation. An example of a time when I expressed my feelings by <u>speaking in generalities</u> is _____

   _____.

   2.   Sometimes we express emotions by indicating that something or someone other than ourselves caused us to feel this way. An example of a time when I expressed my feelings by <u>not owning feelings</u> is_____

   _____.

   3.   Counterfeit emotional language happens when we think we are expressing an emotion and the language we choose does not actually describe what we are feeling. An example of this is _____

   _____.

III.   There are six general guidelines for expressing our emotions more effectively.

   A.   We need to identify what we feel before we try to express it to others. An example of a time when I should have identified my feelings first is _____

   _____.

   B.   Choosing how to communicate our emotions involves assessing our current state as well as selecting an appropriate time and place to discuss our emotions. An example of a time when I should have chosen how to express emotions more carefully is

   _____.

   C.   Use *I* language to express feelings. This reminds us that we own our own emotions and it avoids making others feel defensive. An example of a time when I should have used *I* language is _____

   _____.

   D.   Monitoring how we talk to ourselves about our emotions allows us to gain a better understanding of what we're feeling and whether we want to express it to others. An example of a time when I should have examined my self-talk is _____

   _____.

E.   Adopting a rational–emotive approach to feelings focuses attention on destructive thoughts about emotions that harm the self and relationships with others.

F.   We need to respond sensitively to others when they express their feelings, just as we would like them to respond sensitively to us when we express our emotions. An example of a time when I should have responded more sensitively to someone else's expression of emotion is _____

_____.

Activities

Title	Individual	Partner	Group	Ethno	Internet InfoTrac
4.1 Applying Framing and Feeling Rules	✓	✓	✓		
4.2 The Obstacles We Face	✓	✓	✓	✓	
4.3 Expressing Your Emotions Effectively	✓	✓	✓		
4.4 Identifying Your Emotions and Situations	✓				
4.5 Rating Your Own Level of Emotional Intelligence			✓		✓

Activity 4.1 Applying Framing and Feeling Rules

Purpose: To increase your understanding of framing and feeling rules and their impact on our communication.

Instructions

1.   This activity can be done individually, with a partner, or with a larger study group or class. It can also be posted online for a distance study group.
2.   Read the case study below.
3.   Answer the questions listed below.
4.   Discuss your ideas with your partner or study group.

Example

When a couple gets married, the framing rules define that we are to feel happy. The feeling rules define that we are to express emotions of joy such as laughter, smiling, and goodwill. If you attend a wedding and you experience feelings of sadness instead of joy, you may feel confused. You know that you are supposed to be happy, but that is not how you feel. As a result, you need to do some emotion work in order to work out the difference between what you feel and what society tells you to feel.

Case Study

Imran can't stop thinking about his concerns about the possible new job and new boss. He knows that he is supposed to feel happy, but he cannot shake the uncomfortable feelings he has. Realizing that this is affecting his ability to focus at work and at home, Imran decides that he should talk to someone about his feelings. Imran decides that the best person for him to talk to would be his father as he has a lot of experience in the working world.

That night, Imran sits down with his father. As he starts to tell his father how he feels, tears well up in his eyes. His father raises his hand and tells him to stop crying because he is a man and men are not supposed to cry. They must be strong and in charge of how they feel.

Questions

What is an example of framing rules that you see in this situation?

What is an example of feeling rules that you see in this situation?

What emotion work is taking place?

Activity 4.2 The Obstacles We Face

Purpose: To understand how obstacles can get in the way of your ability to express emotions.

Instructions

1. This activity can be done individually, with a partner, or with a larger study group or class. It can also be posted online for a distance study group.
2. Read the continued story of Imran below.
3. Identify the obstacle that is getting in the way of Imran expressing his emotions.
4. Answer the questions listed below.
5. Discuss your ideas with your partner or study group.

Example

When you choose not to cry in front of your boss, you are experiencing obstacles due to:

- Vulnerability: you do not want to be vulnerable to him or her.
- Professional role: You think that it would be unprofessional to cry at work.

Case Study

Imran brushes away the tears from his face. He suddenly becomes very conscious of his emotions but thinks that he should not express them to his father. He suddenly feels ashamed of himself and realizes that his father is extremely embarrassed by his son's tears. Imran knows that it is very important in his culture for a man to be strong, and he realizes that he has never seen his father cry. He wonders why that is; after all, Imran thinks that people should feel safe enough to cry with their family and friends. He knows that when he is at work, he has to be careful, but he assumed that it was okay to relax with family.

Questions

Imran's father telling Imran that he is not to express emotions about this situation because he is a man is an example of what type of obstacle to expressing emotions?

Imran's worries about his father's embarrassment about his tears is an example of what type of obstacle?

Imran's belief that it is not all right to cry at work is an example of what type of obstacle?

Imran brushing away his tears and feeling ashamed is an example of what type of obstacle?

Activity 4.3 Expressing Your Emotions Effectively

Purpose: To practise expressing emotions effectively and to identify ineffective expressions of emotion.

Instructions

1. This activity can be done individually, with a partner, or with a larger study group or class. It can also be posted online for a distance study group.
2. For each of the statements below, identify why it is an ineffective strategy for expressing emotions.
3. Rewrite the statement to be a more effective expression of emotion.

Example

Expression: "I am angry."

Form of Ineffective Expression: speaking in generalities.

More Effective Expression: "I am frustrated with myself because I knew the answer to that question and could not recall it during the exam."

Expression: "You're a great person."

Expression: "I'm sad."

Expression: "I feel good."

Expression: "I think we're missing the point."

Expression: "I could kill Abhik."

Expression: "I've felt better."

Expression: "I think we should go to the movies."

Activity 4.4 Identifying Your Emotions and Situations

Purpose: To identify your emotions and situations that are appropriate for expressing those emotions.

Instructions
1.   Below is a list of emotions some people experience. To the left of each emotion is a line. If you experience this emotion, place an "X" on the line.
2.   For those emotions you experience, list a situation appropriate for expressing the emotion on the line to the right of the emotion.

Experience	**Emotion**	**Situation**
_____	Anger	_____
_____	Anxiety	_____
_____	Apathy	_____
_____	Depression	_____
_____	Disappointment	_____
_____	Embarrassment	_____
_____	Envy	_____
_____	Gratitude	_____
_____	Guilt	_____
_____	Happiness	_____
_____	Hope	_____

_____   Hopelessness   _____

_____   Insecurity   _____

_____   Joy   _____

_____   Loneliness   _____

_____   Passion   _____

_____   Peace   _____

_____   Pressure   _____

_____   Sadness   _____

_____   Security   _____

_____   Shame   _____

_____   Surprise   _____

_____   Suspicion   _____

_____   Sympathy   _____

_____   Tenderness   _____

_____   Uncertainty   _____

_____   Vindictiveness   _____

_____   Weariness   _____

_____   Yearning   _____

What do the emotions you checked and situations you generated say about who you are?

What do the emotions you did not check say about who you are?

For what kinds of situations would you expect the remaining emotions to be appropriate?

Activity 4.5 Rating Your Own Level of Emotional Intelligence

Purpose: To gain an understanding of your own level of emotional intelligence.

Instructions

1.   This activity can be done individually, with a partner, or with a larger study group or class. It can also be posted online for a distance study group.
2.   Go to the web site http://www.helpself.com/iq-test.htm.
3.   Complete the test and compare your results with those of your partner, group, or class.
4.   What do you think you need to do to improve your emotional intelligence?

Chapter 5: The World of Words

I. Our language and many of our nonverbal behaviours are symbolic.

  A. Symbols are <u>arbitrary</u>; there is no natural connection between the symbol and what it represents, so at any point in time, the symbol or what it represents could change. An example of a symbol whose meaning has changed over time is _____

_____.

  B. Symbols are <u>ambiguous</u> because we have unique individual experiences; there is a range of meanings on which most members of a culture agree. An example of a time when I interpreted a symbol differently than someone else is _____

_____.

  C. Symbols are not tangible or concrete—they are abstract; we do not touch symbols the same way we may touch the things (e.g., a chair or computer) they represent.

II. The principles of verbal communication give us an understanding of how symbols work.

  A. Because language and culture are intricately connected, we learn a set of values, perspectives, and beliefs when we learn to speak or read. Growing up, I learned that _____ indicated we value _____

_____.

  B. Because there are no single definitions for symbols, we must interpret them in the context of the present interaction to attach meaning.

  C. Communication rules help us develop shared understandings of what is happening in a particular interaction.

      1.   <u>Regulative rules</u> help us manage the when, how, where, and with whom we talk about certain things. A regulative rule I usually follow is _____

_____.

      2.   <u>Constitutive rules</u> define what messages mean, or what communication is expected in a particular situation. For me, the following behaviours constitute good student:

_____

_____.

D.   <u>Punctuation</u> creates outer limits for what constitutes the beginning and ending of an interpersonal interaction. An example of a time when punctuation differences created a misunderstanding is _____

_____.

      1.   A common pattern of conflict involving two people punctuating interaction differently is the demand–withdraw cycle.

      2.   Punctuation depends on subjective perceptions.

III.   The ability to use and understand symbols has an impact on the lives we lead.

      A.   We use symbols to define experiences, people, relationships, feelings, and thoughts.

      1.   The names or labels we attach to people, objects, or events highlight some aspects and de-emphasize others.

      2.   Our names or labels can highlight just one aspect of a person, object, or event. An example of a time when I used language to totalize someone is

_____.

3.   The language we use to define relationships shapes how we view and act in those relationships.

B.   Language is value-laden and not neutral.

1.   The judgments and values that appear in our language choices affect how we view or perceive people, objects, and events. An example of a time when <u>language values</u> affected my perceptions is _____

_____.

2.   Loaded language strongly affects our perceptions, usually by creating inaccurate negative connotations. An example of <u>loaded language</u> I recently heard is _____

_____.

3.   Language can degrade others because we are influenced by the names we have for things. An example of <u>degrading language</u> I recently heard is_____

_____.

C.   Symbols help us organize information and perceptions into categories so that we do not have to remember every aspect of every person, object, and event we encounter.

1.   Being able to use language to organize information and perceptions allows for abstract thought.

2.   In categorizing information and perceptions, language can stereotype, which distorts thinking. One time that I used language to <u>stereotype</u> is _____

_____, and my thinking was distorted in this way: _____

_____.

D.   We can use symbols to label things that have happened in the past, are happening now, and might happen in the future.

E.   Symbols allow us to examine our actions so that we can monitor our behaviour in a particular situation as well as manage the impression we make on others.

IV.   When a group of people share a set of norms about how to talk and the purpose talk serves, they form what is called a <u>speech community</u>.

A.   Different speech communities use symbols in different ways.

B.   Speech communities are defined by shared ideas of how to communicate, not by geographic locations.

C.   Individuals are socialized into gender speech communities at a young age.

V.   We can use a set of guidelines for making our verbal communication more effective.

A.   Engaging in dual perspective, or walking in the shoes of another person to see the situation as she or he sees it, requires us to create and interpret messages with both our view and the other's view in mind. An example of a time when I should have used <u>dual perspective</u> is _____

_____.

B.   Recognize that starting sentences with "I" instead of "You" leads us to take responsibility for our thoughts and feelings rather than blaming others for them. An example of a time when owning my thoughts and feelings would have been more effective is _____

_____.

C. Respecting what others say about their thoughts and feelings allows us to confirm rather than disconfirm them, and helps us engage in dual perspective. An example of a time when I should have used this guideline is _____

_____.

D. Because symbols are arbitrary, ambiguous, and abstract, we need to find ways to make our communication more accurate and concrete as is necessary for the situation at hand. An example of a time when my communication lacked clarity and/or accuracy is

_____

_____.

1. Awareness of the levels of abstraction can help make our communication more accurate.

2. Using qualifying language reminds us of the limitations of a message.

3. Indexing reminds us that our evaluations should be applied only to a particular time and situation. An example of when I didn't use indexing was _____

_____.

To use indexing, I would have said _____

_____.

Activities

Title	Individual	Partner	Group	Ethno	Internet InfoTrac
5.1 Applying Communicative Rules	✓	✓	✓	✓	
5.2 Identifying Sexist and Racist Language	✓	✓	✓	✓	
5.3 Learning to Use I Language	✓				
5.4 Recognizing Ambiguity in Verbal Language	✓				
5.5 Emoticons as Symbols of Our Language	✓	✓	✓		✓

Activity 5.1 Applying Communicative Rules

Purpose: To learn to recognize the communication rules that people live by and understand the differences that exist and why they do.

Instructions
1.   This activity can be done individually, with a partner, or with a larger study group or class.
2.   Review the case study of Imran that is presented below.
3.   Answer the questions listed below.
4.   Discuss your answers with a partner or study group.
5.   How were your answers the same or different?
6.   If they were different, why do you think that is?

Example
Communication rules vary across culture and families. These rules tell us what kind of communication is appropriate, at what times, and with whom. They also tell us how to interpret the communication. In some cultures and families, for example, it is considered inappropriate for women to display anger. Discussion about this topic will reveal the underlying messages that are communicated to each of us about the rules that govern our communication patterns.

Case Study
Imran feels very confused. He reviews what has happened over the past week in order to try to understand why he is feeling confused and what is happening to him.

1.   He is offered the possibility of a new job.
2.   He feels excited about the job but has some concerns about it.
3.   He does not talk about it with anyone because he knows there are still several steps in the process to go through.
4.   He knows that it would be inappropriate to talk with any of his colleagues about the job possibility.
5.   He decides to talk with his father about his feelings of confusion.
6.   He starts to cry when he talks to his dad, and he realizes that his father is very uncomfortable with his tears.
7.   His father tells him that he should not be crying about this as he is a man and this is not what men do when they are upset.
8.   Imran now feels further confused as he does not know who he can speak with about how he feels.

Questions

What communication rules is Imran following?

Find one example of a regulative rule that is clear in the case study.

Find one example of a constitutive rule that is clear in the case study.

What factors do you think influence the communication rules?

Compare your results with those of your partner or colleague. What do you attribute any differences to?

Activity 5.2 Identifying Sexist and Racist Language

Purpose: To increase awareness of how language may be perceived as sexist or racist by some people.

Instructions
1. This activity can be done individually, with a partner, or with a larger study group or class.
2. Read the sentences below.
3. For each one, indicate whether you think it includes language that is sexist or racist by writing an "S" for sexist or an "R" for racist in the blank at the left.
4. For any sentences that you think contain sexist or racist language, write out a revised sentence that avoids sexism and racism.
5. Compare your results with those of other students.
6. Generate a list of other sentences that are sexist or racist.

Example
"I now pronounce you man and wife." This is sexist language because the sentence refers to the male as a *man* and the woman as a *wife*. The revision would be "I now pronounce you husband and wife."

_____ "The waitress took our order."

_____ "He's the black sheep of the family."

_____ "Anne is a woman doctor."

_____ "It's okay to tell white lies."

_____ "Edward babysat his son while his wife was away on business."

_____ "Good guys wear white hats."

_____ "A lot of Asians are really just like regular people."

_____ "She's in a black mood—stay away from her until she gets over it."

_____ "The partners in the law firm are Mr. Thompson, Mr. Flagler, Mr. Winstead and Emily."

_____ "Asians are so indirect and deferential."

_____ "The men are ordering chicken wings, and the girls are ordering salads."

Activity 5.3 Learning to Use I *Language*

Purpose: To give you experience in using *I* language.

Instructions

1. This activity can be done individually, with a partner, or with a larger study group or class.
2. Read each of the 10 statements below.
3. Each one relies on *you* language
4. Rephrase each statement so that it is expressed using *I* language

Example
"Your stubbornness makes me angry."
Rephrasing: "I get angry when you are stubborn."

1. "You are so arrogant."

    Rephrasing:

2. "You embarrassed me in front of my friends."

    Rephrasing:

3. "You make me feel guilty."

    Rephrasing:

4. "You get me so upset that I forget things."

    Rephrasing:

5. "You're so inconsiderate of me."
   Rephrasing:

6. "You're very loving."
   Rephrasing:

7. "You're insensitive."
   Rephrasing:

8. "You're so understanding about my situation."
   Rephrasing:

9. "You really are self-centred."
   Rephrasing:

10. "You're very helpful when I talk to you about problems."
    Rephrasing:

Activity 5.4 Recognizing Ambiguity in Verbal Language

Purpose: To provide you with an opportunity to recognize the ambiguity verbal symbols.

Instructions
1.   Read the statements below.
2.   Write two distinct ways that the sentence may be interpreted.
3.   Compare your results with those of a partner.

Example
"I feel so high."
Interpretation 1: You feel like you are intoxicated.
Interpretation 2: You are located high in a building or are taller than others.

1. "That is one bad woman."

    Interpretation 1:

    Interpretation 2:

2. "How is your grass?"
    Interpretation 1:

    Interpretation 2:

3. "Are you straight?"
    Interpretation 1:

    Interpretation 2:

4. "This is very heavy."
    Interpretation 1:

    Interpretation 2:

5. "It's really hot in here."
    Interpretation 1:

    Interpretation 2:

6. "I don't want you to hit on me."
    Interpretation 1:

    Interpretation 2:

Activity 5.5 Emoticons as Symbols of Our Language

Purpose: To understand how the use of emoticons affects our communication patterns.

Instructions
1. Arrange a time when everyone in your study group can be on a social networking site together.
2. Agree that for 10 minutes you are going to communicate to each other on the site by using emoticons and abbreviations.
3. For a list of possible emoticons and abbreviations to use go to http://writing.colostate.edu/guides/documents/email/com2g2.cfm.
4. After the 10 minutes, switch to using plain words and do not use any emoticons or abbreviations to communicate with each other.
5. What do you notice about the differences in the way that you communicate to each other using those different symbols?

Example
Plain words: "As a matter of fact"
Emoticons and abbreviations format: AAMOF

Chapter 6: Nonverbal Communication

I. Nonverbal and verbal communication are both similar to and different from each other.

    A. Four similarities exist between the two types of communication.

        1. Nonverbal messages are symbolic, arbitrary, ambiguous, and abstract.

        2. Different cultures share rules that help us understand what types of nonverbal communication are appropriate as well as what different nonverbal messages mean. For me, touching someone is appropriate when _____ _____; If a stranger touches me, it means_____ _____.

        3. Nonverbal communication may be intentional or unintentional. An example of a time when I used nonverbal communication intentionally today is _____ _____.

        4. The culture in which we grew up teaches how, when, and where we use nonverbal codes. An example of a nonverbal code that I used when I was younger and use much less or not at all today is _____ _____.

    B. Three differences exist between verbal and nonverbal communication.

        1. Generally, people believe nonverbal communication more than they believe verbal communication, particularly if the two messages contradict each other. An example of a time when I trusted the nonverbal message more than the verbal message is _____ _____.

2.   Nonverbal communication is not limited to a single channel. When I am outside, the nonverbal channel that is most likely to operate is _____

_____.

3.   Nonverbal communication does not have distinct starting and ending points.

II.   Four principles guide our understanding of nonverbal communication.

A.   Nonverbal and verbal communication work together by having the nonverbal message repeat, emphasize, complement, contradict, or substitute for the verbal message.

B.   Nonverbal cues also help regulate the flow of interaction between people. An example of a time when I used nonverbal communication to regulate the conversation is _____

_____.

C.   Nonverbal messages also tend to emphasize the relational level of meaning in an interaction; these include responsiveness, liking, and power. An example of a nonverbal message that indicates responsiveness for me is _____

_____.

An example of a nonverbal cue that indicates liking for me is _____

_____.

An example of a nonverbal cue that indicates power to me is _____

_____.

D.   Nonverbal communication reflects and expresses culture, which means that we learn nonverbal communication over time.

III. There are nine basic types of nonverbal communication.

A.   Kinesics refers to all of our body and facial expressions. My favourite nonverbal kinesic message is _____, and it indicates _____ to those around me.

B. Haptics is the technical term we use to refer to our touching behaviours. In situations, I am most likely to use touch to communicate _____.

C. Physical appearance messages are frequently the first way we form perceptions of others when we meet them. For me, the most important aspect of physical appearance in a potential romantic partner is _____.

D. Artifacts are personal objects that we use to indicate to others important information about our self. The most revealing artifact in my life is _____

_____.

E. Environmental factors are aspects of the communication context that influences how we act and feel. The environmental factors in the classroom we use for this class indicate _____

_____ to me.

F. Proxemics is the technical term for space and how we use it. Where I live, I/we use space to indicate _____.

G. How we use and value time is the study of chronemics. For me, being late usually indicates _____; I tend to arrive for class _____ minutes early/late (circle one).

H. Messages that we indicate with our voice, beyond the words we use, are called paralinguistics.

I. Silence is the final type of nonverbal message. I like to use silence to indicate _____

_____.

IV. Two guidelines help us use and interpret nonverbal communication more effectively.

A. We need to use monitoring skills. An example of a time when I should have used monitoring to be more effective was _____

_____.

B.   We need to exert caution by enacting personal and contextual qualifications. An example of a time when I should have interpreted nonverbal messages more cautiously is _____ _____.

Activities

Title	Individual	Partner	Group	Ethno	Internet InfoTrac
6.1 Case Study	✓	✓	✓	✓	
6.2 Portrait of Myself	✓	✓	✓		
6.3 Nonverbal Designs	✓	✓	✓	✓	
6.4 Identifying Nonverbal Cues	✓	✓	✓	✓	
6.5 Feng Shui and Forms of Nonverbal Communication	✓	✓	✓	✓	✓

Activity 6.1 Case Study

Purpose: To learn to recognize the nonverbal communication methods in everyday communication between people.

Instructions
1.   This activity can be done individually, with a partner, or with a larger study group or class.
2.   Review the case study of Imran that is presented below.
3.   After you have read the story, answer the questions below.
4.   Discuss your answers with a partner or study group.
5.   How were your answers the same or different?
6.   If they were different, why do you think that is?

Example
When a person wears a cross as a piece of jewellery, it is considered an artifact. This artifact is often associated with religion, and people usual infer from this artifact that the person who is wearing it is religious.

Case Study
The next day, Imran wakes up feeling tired and headachy. He decides that he is going to dress casually today as he is too tired to put on his normal shirt and tie. He considers whether it would be okay if he wore jeans to work. He sees other people at the office doing this, but he has never done it before. As he is leaving his house, he sees his lucky key chain hanging by the front door, grabs it, and puts it in his pocket. He thinks to himself that right now he needs all of the good luck he can get. Imran walks slowly toward the bus station. Normally he walks very quickly, and people always comment on how he looks as though he is in a hurry. Today he can feel his feet dragging, and he knows that at the pace he is going, he will miss the next bus. He hopes that the bus driver will wait for him if he waves his hand out to him. He does not like to be late for work. One of his office mates is always late for work, and everyone notices it. Imran does not want to be talked about by other people in that way.

As Imran gets on the bus, he heads for a seat at the back of the bus. He sees an empty seat, sits down on it, and puts his briefcase on the seat beside him. Although he knows he should leave the seat open for someone else, he really does not feel like sharing his seat with anyone today. Imran looks around the bus and starts to think about all of the people who are on the bus every day. It is always very crowded, and no one ever looks at each other. It is very quiet on the bus, and the lack of sound is quite obvious. He wonders if these people would be friendlier and talk with each other if they were in a less crowded space or not on public transit. He notices one man and woman talking quietly to each other. The woman puts her hand on the man's shoulder and starts to rub his back. He wonders what they are talking about. Lost in his thoughts about this, he does not notice that someone is trying to sit in the seat beside him. It is only when he hears the person clear her throat that he looks up to see an old high school friend of his trying to get his attention.

Questions

There are at least nine different forms of nonverbal communication that took place in the case study. How many can you find? What did you interpret from the nonverbal behaviours?

Behaviour   Interpretation

1.
2.
3.
4.
5.
6.
7.
8.
9.

Did the behaviours highlight, substitute, repeat, contradict, or complement the verbal communication?

Behaviour   What purpose did the behaviour serve?

1.
2.
3.
4.
5.
6.
7.
8.
9.

Activity 6.2 Portrait of Myself

Purpose: To increase your awareness of the ways in which you use artifacts to personalize your environment.

Instructions
1. This activity can be done individually, with a partner, or with a study group.
2. Go to your dormitory room or your room in your home or apartment.
3. Using the space below, list the personal artifacts you have put there.
4. Do not list any that you didn't select to be in your home/space.
5. Beside each item that you list, explain its significance to you and what it communicates about your identity.
6. Discuss the results with a partner or group.

Example
Photo of me in Nepal

This photograph reminds me of a very special trek I made in Nepal. It also communicates to others that I am adventurous.

Artifact   Significance/What It Communicates

Activity 6.3 Nonverbal Designs

Purpose: To increase your awareness of the ways in which settings influence interaction.

Instructions
1.   This activity can be done individually, with a partner, or with a study group.
2.   Select three restaurants to visit: One should be a very elegant restaurant; one should be an inexpensive fast-food restaurant; and one should be an ethnic restaurant.
3.   Describe the setting of each restaurant by answering the questions in Part A below.
4.   Describe interaction patterns among diners by answering the questions in Part B below.
5.   Discuss possible different interpretations with a partner (Part C).

Example
In fast-food restaurants, the lighting is often quite bright. This tends to communicate an alert, open type of environment. Is that what an elegant restaurant would want to convey? What might that type of restaurant do differently?

PART A: DESCRIPTION OF THE SETTING

What is the average distance between tables or booths?

How is the restaurant lit (candles, soft side lighting, overhead bulbs, fluorescent lighting)?

What kind of music, if any, is playing in the restaurant? Describe the style and tempo of music.

How are members of the staff dressed? Notice the hostess as well as servers. Are they dressed formally or informally? In uniforms or not?

Describe the decor of each restaurant. Identify artwork, if any; quality of carpeting; presence of plants and other items.

PART B: DESCRIPTION OF INTERACTION PATTERNS

What is the average time that diners spend in each restaurant?

What is the average number of people in each party?

How intimate do diners' conversations appear to be, judging from touching, eye behaviour, and other nonverbal cues?

PART C: REFLECTION AND INTERPRETATIONS

Compare your answers with those of a partner. What do the nonverbal messages convey to each of you?

Activity 6.4 Identifying Nonverbal Cues

Purpose: To make you more aware of others' nonverbal cues that lead you to particular interpretations.

Instructions
1.   This activity can be done with a partner or with a study group. Invite group members from different cultures and genders to participate in order to enrich the learning experience.
2.   Using the form below, identify two or more nonverbal behaviours that you associate with the states described on the left.
3.   When you have completed the form, consider whether the nonverbal behaviours you listed might have meanings other than those you assign to them.
4.   Discuss your results with your study group.

Example
Happiness   Smiling, laughing

State   Associated Nonverbal Cues

1. Anger

2. Lack of interest

3. Arrogance

4. Boredom

5. Romantic interest

6. Fear

7. Embarrassment

8. Type A personality

9. Nervous

10. Disapproving

Activity 6.5 Feng Shui and Forms of Nonverbal Communication

Purpose: To learn about intersections between nonverbal communication and the Chinese practice of feng shui.

Instructions
1. This activity can be done individually, with a partner, or with a larger study group or class.
2. Go to YouTube (http://www.youtube.com) and watch a video clip on feng shui.
3. Make a list of the recommendations given for the organization of a house or space.
4. Using the list below, identify what nonverbal messages are being communicated.
5. In your group or using the Internet, identify how different cultures use other symbols or items in the home to communicate certain messages.

Example
An individual was trying to sell her home and was having difficulty with it. A friend of hers suggested that she use feng shui principles in order to transform the "energy" in her house. It was noted that in the centre of the house was a very heavy stone coffee table that hadn't been moved since it had been brought in years before. When the friend had the stone table removed from the house, energies were allowed to flow freely and regenerate. This is an example of the use of environmental factors to communicate certain messages.

What messages did you understand about how to use space in the home?

How do the following concepts apply to feng shui?

➢ Kinesics

➢ Haptics

➤ Physical appearance

➤ Artifacts

➤ Environmental factors

➤ Proxemics

➤ Chronemics

➤ Paralanguage

➤ Silence

Identify how people of other cultures have similar or different "rules" in their homes. For example, some religious people insist on having religious items in their homes to ensure certain messages are given.

Chapter 7: Cultural Diversity and Communication

I. Cultural anthropology describes and seeks to explain similarities and differences in thought and behaviour among groups of humans.

  A. _____ is the learned and shared understanding about how to behave and what has meaning in our lives.

  B. Within a larger society, there are smaller groups of people who have a shared understanding that is unique to them. This is known as a _____.

  C. Ethnic groups are a subculture based on religion, language, common origin or ancestral traditions. Two examples of ethnic groups within Canada are _____ and _____.

  D. The ethnic group that I am a part of is _____.
      Beliefs of my culture include _____.
      A value in my culture is _____.
      A symbol within my culture is _____.

  E. A subculture that I am part of is _____.

  F. Some of the unique characteristics of my subculture are _____

      _____.

II. Nonverbal communication is similar to verbal communication in expressing cultural values. Each culture is unique and has different ways of communicating between its members.

  A. In my culture, we express the following emotions in the following ways:

      Anger: _____

      Greeting: _____

Sadness: _____

Happiness: _____

III.   The study of cultural diversity has emphasized research on cultural values. There are a number of different dimensions from which to view culture.

A.   Time is an aspect of life that is viewed differently across cultures. A culture with a monochronic orientation toward time views time as a valuable commodity to be saved and carefully guarded.

Some examples of this type of thinking in the Canadian culture are the following:

_____
_____
_____

B.   Cultures with a polychromic culture tend to assume a less structured attitude toward time.

Examples of this type of thinking include _____

_____.

C.   Having different orientations toward time could pose a problem when people of two different cultures have to work together.

An example of a possible problem at work might include _____

_____
_____.

D.   High context and low context are terms that are used to describe a society's communication patterns. High context societies put great emphasis on nonverbal and environmental cues to communicate. Low context societies tend to put more emphasis on words and literal meanings in their communication patterns.

An example of a high context society would be _____.

An example of a low context society would be _____.

E.   The dimension of power refers to how a society handles inequality.

    1.   In low power distance nations, inequalities among people tend to be _____

        _____.

    2.   In high power societies, inequalities among people is considered _____

        _____.

    3.   In Canada we tend to have an _____ power distance society. An example

        of this is _____

        _____.

F.   Societies in which ties between people are loose and everyone is expected to look out for
themselves are known as _____ societies.

    1.   Societies that are integrated into strong cohesive groups are known as _____

        _____ societies.

    2.   In Canada we live in a(n) _____ society.

    3.   The benefits of living in a collectivistic society are _____

        _____

        _____.

    4.   The benefits of living in an individualistic society are _____

        _____

        _____.

G.   Masculinity and femininity are another way that societies are defined.

    1.   Features of a masculine society include characteristics such as _____

        _____

        _____.

2.   Features of a feminine society include characteristics such as _____

_____

_____.

H.   The term <u>uncertainty avoidance</u> refers to a society's tolerance for uncertainty. Cultures have strict laws and rules in order to manage the stress that is caused by uncertainty.

1.   Cultures that are more tolerant of different opinions are referred to as _____

_____.

2.   A culture that I think demonstrates uncertainty avoidance is_____

_____.

IV.   The fifth dimension to describe cultures is long-term orientation. This refers to the degree to which a society does or does not value commitment and respect for tradition.

V.   Cultural intelligence refers to a person's capacity to solve problems and adapt to changing situations in cultural contexts. This term reflects how well people are able to empathize, work with, direct, and interact with other people.

A.   A person who I believe has strong cultural intelligence is _____.

B.   This person has demonstrated strong cultural intelligence in the following situation(s):

_____

_____

_____

_____.

C.   I believe that this person fits the _____ profile. My reason for thinking this is _____

_____

_____.

VI.   Cultural intelligence can be developed in both personal and professional lives.

      A.   My cultural intelligence score according to the diagnostic tool in the textbook is as follows:

             Cognitive CQ score   _____

             Physical CQ score   _____

             Emotional/Motivational CQ score   _____

      B.   In order to improve my cognitive CQ, I plan to _____

_____

_____ .

      C.   In order to improve my physical CQ score, I plan to _____

_____

_____ .

      D.   In order to improve my emotional/motivational CQ score, I plan to _____

_____

_____ .

Activities

Title	Individual	Partner	Group	Ethno	Internet InfoTrac
7.1 Applying the Concepts to a Case Study	✓	✓	✓		
7.2 Understanding the Underlying Meaning	✓	✓	✓		✓
7.3 Cultural Greetings	✓	✓	✓	✓	✓
7.4 Understanding Individualistic and Collectivist Cultures	✓	✓	✓	✓	✓
7.5 The Development of Cultural Competence in the Workplace	✓	✓	✓	✓	✓

Activity 7.1 Applying the Concepts to a Case Study

Purpose: To gain an understanding of how to apply the concepts of cross-cultural communication.

Instructions

1. This activity can be done individually, with a partner, or with a larger study group or class.
2. Review the case study of Imran that is presented below.
3. After you have read the story, answer the questions below.
4. Discuss your answers with your partner or study group.
5. How were your answers the same or different?
6. If they were different, why do you think that is?

Example

In the classroom, you are sitting beside a woman who is covered from head to toe. The teacher asks you to turn to the person and introduce yourself. Normally you shake hands with people when you meet. In this situation, you follow the woman's lead as you recognize that she may not be comfortable shaking your hand. This is an example of being culturally sensitive or having cultural intelligence.

Case Study

Imran removes his briefcase and smiles hello to his friend Sajida. He has not seen her since high school and looks forward to talking with her about what she has been up to. Imran notices that she is still wearing the same headscarf that she wore in high school. He can't remember where she is from and feels embarrassed by his ignorance. He goes to shake her hand, but she draws back slightly and shakes her head no. He then remembers that she is Muslim and from India. He feels uncomfortable because he does not want to offend her by doing something inappropriate. Although he is also from India, he was raised Christian. He wishes he could remember more about her culture.

Sajida tells him that she is still at university as she is doing her master's in mathematics. She says that her father is very disapproving of her studies because he wants her to get married and start to have children. She says that her father believes he is supposed to decide the future of his children, and he is not very supportive of her decision.

Imran thinks he is lucky to have the parents he has. He is a first-generation Canadian, and his parents allowed him to adopt the norms and values of Canada. He shakes his head sadly at Sajida to show his support of her. He notices that she does not meet his eyes and wonders if that is because she is sad or if she is not supposed to look at him since he is male. He asks her more questions but notices that the more questions he asks, the quieter she gets. He wonders if he has offended her. Not knowing what more to say, Imran is relieved to see that he is at his bus stop.

He indicates to Sajida that he must get off and goes to give her a "high five" goodbye. Once again, she pulls away, and Imran feels like kicking himself for his thoughtlessness.

Questions for Discussion

What differences did you notice between Imran's and Sajida's greetings?

What nonverbal messages did Sajida give regarding her culture?

What differences did you notice in their styles of talking with each other?

What cultural values of Sajida do you know based on this case study?

Using the dimensions of culture, describe one of the factors that Sajida is influenced by.

Was Imran showing cultural intelligence? Why or why not?

What could Imran have done differently?

Activity 7.2 Understanding the Underlying Meaning

Purpose: To understand how communication reflects and expresses cultural values.

Instructions

1. This activity can be done individually, with a partner, or with a larger study group. It can also be posted online for a distance study group.
2. Review the list of idioms below.
3. Create a possible interpretation of the idioms based upon your own culture and language.
4. Compare your results with those of your peers.
5. Use the Internet to validate the meaning of the statement.
6. How does the idiom reflect the values of that culture?

Example

Idiom: *Milk from the foot of the cow.*

Possible interpretation: It is impossible to do this.

Actual meaning: Extremely fresh milk (from Chile)

Reflection of cultural values: Reflects the agricultural roots of the country.

Statements

Idiom: *There'll be wigs on the green.*

Possible interpretation:

Actual meaning:

Reflection of cultural values:

Idiom: *They left us in the ha'penny place.*

Possible interpretation:

Actual meaning:

Reflection of cultural values:

Idiom: *Not only butchers carry big knives.*

Possible interpretation:

Actual meaning:

Reflection of the cultural values:

Idiom: *Your car is a bit down in the teeth.*

Possible interpretation:

Actual meaning:

Reflection of cultural values:

Idiom: *That's not my cup of tea.*

Possible interpretation:

Actual meaning:

Reflection of cultural values:

Idiom: *I'm on a sticky wicket.*

Possible interpretation:

Actual meaning:

Reflection of cultural values:

Activity 7.3 Cultural Greetings

Purpose: To gain an understanding of how different cultures use verbal and nonverbal methods to communicate hello to each other.

Instructions

1. This activity can be done individually, with a partner, or with a larger study group or class.
2. Identify five people you know who come from cultures other than your own.
3. Ask each person about his or her cultural practices of greeting each other.
4. Record the responses.
5. Compare the results of your findings with other members of your group or class.
6. If you do not know five individuals from different cultures, this exercise can be done on the Internet using a search engine to locate different cultural norms.

Example

In the French Canadian culture, it is common to greet a person by kissing both of his or her cheeks.

Person #1:

Culture:

Standard greeting:

Person #2:

Culture:

Standard greeting:

Person #3:

Culture:

Standard greeting:

Person #4:

Culture:

Standard greeting:

Person #5:

Culture:

Standard greeting:

Activity 7.4 Understanding Individualistic and Collectivist Cultures

Purpose: To gain an understanding of the significance of the differences between individualistic and collectivist cultures and how they influence relationships.

Instructions

1. This activity can be done individually, with a partner, or with a class or study group. It can also be posted online for a discussion.
2. Below is a list of some of the different ethnic groups that reside in Canada.
3. Find one person from each of these ethnic groups.
4. Ask them if their culture is individualistic or collectivist. You may need to explain to them the differences, which will assist with your own integration of the material.
5. Ask them for examples to support the determination of the individualistic versus collectivist culture.
6. How does this orientation affect their relationships with other people?
7. Use the form on the next page to document your findings.
8. If you cannot find a person from a particular ethnic group, refer to the Internet and complete research there to determine the answer.
9. Discuss your findings with your partner or classmates.

Example

Culture (Person)	Individualism or Collectivism	Impact on Relationships
Southeast Asia (Suki)	Collectivist culture. Family is extremely important and is considered to be the focus of many important decisions.	Suki will consult with her family, including her parents, when she has any important decision to make in her life.

Culture (Person)	Individualism or Collectivism (provide examples)	Impact on Relationships
French		
German		
Chinese		
Native Canadian		
Ukrainian		
Southeast Indian		
Jamaican		
African		

Activity 7.5 The Development of Cultural Competence in the Workplace

Purpose: To understand the role that organizations have to play in developing culturally competent workplaces and employees.

Instructions

1. This activity can be done individually, with a partner, or with a larger group or class.
2. Select a national organization, institution, or company to investigate.
3. Arrange to meet with someone from the organization who can tell you about the initiatives the organization has taken toward being culturally competent.
4. Review the factors listed below to identify if the organization is accomplishing the goal of being culturally competent.
5. Track your findings on the form on the next page.
6. Discuss your findings with your partner or group.

Example

The Bank of Montreal (BMO) has received awards for the changes it has made to become a more culturally competent organization. It has formally adopted a proactive stance toward equity by creating the Office of Workplace Diversity and Equity. See the following link for more details:
http://www2.bmo.com/bmo/files/images/7/1/Reissue_Minorities_ENG_Nov.pdf.

Issue	What the Organization Has Done	The Organization's Plans to Address This Issue
Does the organization have a policy on equity and diversity? If so, what is it?		
How many different cultural groups are represented in the organization? What types of positions do these people hold? Is the management staff reflective of the diversity of the organization?		
What specific things has the organization done to encourage an equitable and diverse workplace?		
What barriers does the organization face in creating a diverse and equitable workforce?		

Chapter 8: Mindful Listening

I.   Listening is a process that involves our ears, minds, and hearts; hearing is an activity that involves sound waves stimulating our eardrums.

    A.   Being mindful involves paying complete attention to what is happening in an interaction at that moment in time without imposing our own thoughts, feelings, or judgments on others.

    B.   Hearing is when we receive the sound waves.

    C.   To listen, we also need to select and organize the many stimuli that are part of a conversation.

    D.   Once we select, take in, and organize the stimuli, we attach meaning to the messages.

    E.   As we engage in communication, we use both verbal and nonverbal means to indicate we are listening.

    F.   After a particular interaction has ended, remembering what was exchanged is the last part of the listening process.

II.   There are two main categories of obstacles or barriers to effective listening. In addition, at times we do not listen at all.

    A.   Obstacles within the situation (external factors) are those situational factors we cannot control.

        1.   <u>Message overload</u> occurs because we cannot take in all communication with the same level of mindfulness. An example of a time when I experienced message overload recently is _____

_____.

2. <u>Message complexity</u> occurs when the messages are too detailed, use technical terms, or contain many difficult connections between the various sentence parts. An example of when I tuned out but should not have because of message complexity is _____

_____.

3. <u>Noise</u> is any verbal or nonverbal stimuli in the environment that keeps us from being good listeners. An example of noise that occurred in one of my interactions today is _____

_____.

B. The other set of listening barriers is those that we as individuals can control (internal factors).

1. <u>Preoccupation</u> happens when we are so caught up in what is happening with ourselves that we forget to pay careful attention to what is happening in our interaction with others. An example of preoccupation in my life occurred when _____

_____.

2. <u>Prejudgment</u> happens when we think we know what others are going to say before they say it or we tune them out because we believe they have nothing to offer. I engaged in prejudgment when I _____

_____.

3. Emotionally loaded language can "push our buttons," either positively or negatively, and we end up tuning out the other person. An example of emotionally loaded language is _____

_____.

4. Because effective listening requires so much energy, there are times when a lack of effort (time or energy) hinders us. An example of a time when I didn't put forth the required listening effort is _____

_____.

5. Sometimes we forget that different types of interactions call for different types of listening; similarly, we sometimes forget that people with different experiences have learned different speaking and listening styles.

C. In addition to barriers to listening, there are times when we engage in nonlistening behaviours.

1. Pseudolistening is when we pretend that we are paying full attention to a communication interaction. An example of a time when I engaged in pseudolistening is _____

_____.

2. Monopolizing occurs when we are constantly trying to redirect the communication back to ourselves and our concerns without giving others the opportunity to complete their thoughts. An example of a time when I engaged in monopolizing is _____

_____.

3.   Selective listening happens when we focus only on certain aspects of a conversation, either those with which we do not agree or those that do not interest us at the moment. I engaged in selective listening when I _____

_____.

4.   We engage in defensive listening when we assume a message has negative connotations (relational-level meanings) even though the person did not intend to criticize, attack, or be hostile toward us. An example of defensive listening was when I _____.

5.   When we ambush another person, we listen only for information that will help us attack the other person and/or that person's ideas. An example of ambushing is when _____.

6.   Literal listening is ignoring the relational level of meaning. I have seen literal listening in _____ situations.

III.   In different situations, we listen to accomplish different communication goals.

A.   Sometimes we are interested in the pleasure or enjoyment we receive from listening to a particular type of communication. I like to listen to _____

_____ for pleasure.

B.   To gather and evaluate information others provide, we need to be mindful, control obstacles, ask questions, and create devices to help us remember and organize information. I listen to _____

_____ to gather and evaluate information.

C.   Listening to support others requires that we be mindful, avoid judgment, understand the other person's perspective on the situation, paraphrase what has been said to check the accuracy of our interpretations, use minimal encouragers, ask questions, and support the person even if we do not support the content or ideas expressed. I listen to support others when I _____

_____.

IV.   Three listening guidelines reinforce effective practices.

   A.   Being mindful involves listening fully to what is happening. An example of a time
         when my communication would have been more effective if I had been mindful is

         _____

         _____.

   B.   Adapting our listening to the situation at hand, our goals, the others' goals, and the
         individuals involved makes us better able to understand and respond appropriately
         during and after the interaction. An example of a time when I should have adapted my
         listening is _____

         _____.

   C.   Putting forth the necessary effort to listen actively focuses our attention on the
         communication and away from the potential distractions or barriers we often
         encounter. An example of a time when I should have put forth more effort to listen
         actively is _____

         _____.

Activities

Title	Individual	Partner	Group	Ethno	Internet InfoTrac
8.1 Case Study: Obstacles to Listening	✓	✓	✓		
8.2 Obstacles to Listening		✓	✓		
8.3 Learning to Paraphrase	✓	✓	✓		
8.4 Identifying Forms of Nonlistening	✓	✓	✓		✓
8.5 Listening Styles			✓	✓	

Activity 8.1 Case Study: Obstacles to Listening

Purpose: To learn to apply the concepts of obstacles to listening.

Instructions

1. This activity can be done individually, with a partner, or with a larger study group or class.
2. Review the case study of Imran that is presented below.
3. After you have read the story, answer the questions below.
4. Discuss your answers with a partner or study group.
5. How were your answers the same or different?
6. If they were different, why do you think that is?

Example

You find that when you are in class, you don't always listen to the instructor. You may find yourself thinking about the class that came before, the kids you have to pick up from day-care, or the groceries you need to buy. In this example of nonlistening, the obstacles are preoccupation and psychological noise.

Case Study

As Imran gets off the bus, he is still thinking a great deal about the conversation he had with Sajida. He thinks about his life and his current job scenario and realizes that he should be very grateful for all that he has. He bumps into his friend Rick as he walks along. Rick is a very chatty person and always has many stories to tell, usually about the wild night he had the night before. Imran finds these stories very tedious to listen to as they are always the same, just a different bar and different group of people. As Rick starts to talk, Imran finds himself wondering why Rick would waste so much money and time going to bars. It seems so ridiculous. He hears Rick say, "You know what I mean, Imran?" Imran realizes that he did not hear a word that Rick said before that, so he answers with a quick "Oh, yeah, sure," meanwhile wondering what it was that he has agreed to.

Questions for Reflection

Does Imran demonstrate good listening skills in this scenario? What indications do you have to support this?

List the obstacles that are affecting Imran's ability to listen.

What could Imran do to improve his listening skills in such a situation?

Activity 8.2 Obstacles to Listening

Purpose: To understand and identify the obstacles to effective listening.

Instructions

1. This activity can be done with a partner or with a larger study group or class.
2. One person is to read the message below one time.
3. The other person (people) is responsible for listening to the message.
4. The listeners are not allowed to ask any questions and are not allowed to use any tools such as paper to write out notes.
5. Each person is to describe what they remember of the message.
6. After completing the exercise, reflect on and discuss your listening skills using the debriefing questions as your guide.

Example

You are sitting on the subway with a friend. It is a busy subway and there are many people lined up side by side. As your friend starts to tell you her story of the date she was on the night before, you become aware that someone else on the subway is listening to the story. You feel uncomfortable and find yourself distracted and unable to focus on what your friend is telling you. This is an example of an internal obstacle known as preoccupation.

Message

Gene thought a lot about what he wanted to do after college. He finally decided that he would go to law school in order to become a public defender. Last semester, Gene sent in applications to eight law schools. So far, he has received rejections from three of them and acceptances from two of them. The other three schools haven't contacted him one way or the other.

The problem Gene now faces is that both of the schools that have accepted him require his answer (yes or no) by the end of the month. The three schools he hasn't heard from are higher on his list of preferred schools than the two that have accepted him. He's not sure whether to take one of the sure bets or hold out in the hopes that he will be accepted by a better school. He is further confused because the first two schools offered him scholarships of $5,000 and $7,000, respectively.

Debriefing Questions

What internal obstacles got in the way of your listening process?

What external obstacles got in the way of your listening process?

What tools did you use to remember the details?

What could you have done differently to make it easier for you to remember the details of the story?

Activity 8.3 Learning to Paraphrase

Purpose: To give you experience in using paraphrasing.

Instructions
For each of the statements below, write a paraphrase that aims to clarify and check perceptions of what others say. Try to paraphrase in ways that reflect both the thoughts and feelings of the person speaking.

Example
Statement: I think we're seeing too much of each other
Paraphrase: So you want us to get together less frequently?

Statements
"I really like communication, but what could I do with a major in this field?"

Paraphrase:

"I don't know if Pat and I are getting too serious too fast."

Paraphrase:

"You can borrow my car if you really need to, but please be careful with it. I can't afford any repairs, and if you have an accident, I won't be able to drive to Toronto this weekend."

Paraphrase:

"I feel like I am going crazy. Every time I turn around, there is another thing to do, and I can't keep myself organized."

Paraphrase:

Activity 8.4 Identifying Forms of Nonlistening

Purpose: To give you experience in recognizing forms of ineffective listening in everyday situations.

Instructions
1. This activity can be done with a partner or with a larger study group or class.
2. Go to the Internet and watch a videotaped political debate for 15 minutes.
3. What forms of nonlistening do you see the politicians using?
4. What is the impact of the nonlistening that you observe?

Example
When politicians are debating on a heated topic, they often engage in defensive and ambushing styles of nonlistening. They do this as a way to gain power in the dialogue.

Form of nonlistening:

Impact:

Form of nonlistening:

Impact:

Form of nonlistening:

Impact:

Form of nonlistening:

Impact:

Form of nonlistening:

Impact:

Activity 8.5 Listening Styles

Purpose: To understand the need to be aware of how different people from different cultures and backgrounds use listening skills in different ways.

Instructions

1. Gather a small group of individuals from your class who are from at least three different cultures.
2. Review the basic listening skills of attending, mindfulness, and active listening (e.g., paraphrasing, asking questions, and summarizing).
3. Discuss with the group how each of you uses these listening skills.
4. What rules of communication are you following?
5. If you are talking in your native language, do you use the same listening skills?
6. What differences and similarities are there between cultures in the way they express active listening?

Chapter 9: Communication Climate: The Foundation of Personal Relationships

I.   Four elements contribute to satisfying personal relationships.

    A.   <u>Investments</u> are the contributions (e.g., time, energy, emotions) that we make to relationships without expecting to get them back if the relationship ends; in the most satisfying relationships, everyone feels that the investments made by all involved are roughly equal. My relationship with _____ is an example of one of equal investment.

    B.   <u>Commitment</u> is the personal choice we make to keep a personal relationship alive in the future. An example of how I show commitment in a personal relationship is by _____ _____.

    C.   <u>Trust</u> develops in a relationship as the people involved do what they say they will do and support each other. An example of a relationship in which I did not trust the other person is _____ _____.

    D.   <u>Relational dialectics</u> are the opposing forces or tensions that crop up in everyday relational functioning.

        1.   We need to address our desire for independence (autonomy) and interdependence (connection).

        2.   We need to address our desire for what is familiar or habitual (predictability) and what is new or different (novelty).

        3.   We need to address our desire for open communication (openness) and privacy (closedness).

        4.   We can manage these tensions by neutralizing them, selecting one over the other, separating one from the other into different aspects of our lives, and reframing the tensions by redefining what the tensions mean to us.

II.   Different types of communication create supportive and defensive climates in personal relationships.

    A.   Interpersonal climates occur on a continuum from confirming to disconfirming.

    B.   <u>Confirming messages</u> recognize that another person exists, acknowledge that another matters to us, and endorse what we believe is true. An example of a confirming message I recently experienced is _____

_____.

    C.   <u>Disconfirming messages</u> deny the person's existence, indicate the other person does not matter to us, and reject another person's feelings or thoughts. An example of a disconfirming message I recently experienced is _____

_____.

    D.   There are six types of communication that create supportive and defensive relational climates.

        1.   We create supportive climates when we describe behaviours and others; we create defensive climates when we judge or evaluate others.

        2.   We create supportive climates when we communicate openness to a variety of points of view; we create defensive climates when we use language that indicates there is only one way to view a situation (e.g., it's my way or the highway).

        3.   We create supportive climates when our communication feels open, honest, and spontaneous; we create defensive climates when our communication feels manipulative, premeditated, and strategic.

        4.   We create supportive climates when we use communication to find ways of satisfying everyone involved in the interaction; we create defensive climates when we try to control, triumph over, or manipulate others, what they think, and what they do.

        5.   We create supportive climates when we demonstrate empathy or care about the other person; we create defensive climates when we act in a neutral, detached, or indifferent way.

6.   We create supportive climates when we use communication to indicate that all parties are equal; we create defensive climates when we use communication to indicate that one person is superior to another.

III.   There are at least six guidelines for building and sustaining healthy relational and communication climates.

   A.   Monitor our communication so that we use it to create supportive rather than defensive climates. An example of a time when I could have used the information I know now to build or sustain a relationship is _____

      _____.

   B.   We need to accept and confirm others while still being honest. An example of a time when I should have been more accepting or more honest is _____

      _____.

   C.   We need to make sure we confirm and assert (state what we need, feel, or want without putting ourselves above or below others) ourselves in a relationship. An example of a time when I should have asserted myself in a relationship is _____

      _____.

   D.   We need to self-disclose when it is appropriate and use caution when choosing how much, when, and to whom to disclose. An example of a time when I should have disclosed more/less (circle one) is _____

      _____.

   E.   We need to understand that there is not a single mould into which all relationships fit. An example of a time when I should have recognized and respected the diversity in relationships is _____

      _____.

   F.   We need to find ways to respond effectively to criticism. An example of a time when I could have responded more constructively to criticism is _____

      _____.

Activities

Title	Individual	Partner	Group	Ethno	Internet InfoTrac
9.1 Case Study: Understanding Supportive Communication	✓	✓	✓	✓	
9.2 Features of Relationships	✓				
9.3 Increasing Your Awareness of Self-Disclosure Risk Levels	✓	✓	✓	✓	
9.4 Distinguishing Aggressive, Assertive, and Deferential Forms of Communication	✓				
9.5 Rating the Supportiveness of Communication Climates	✓	✓	✓		✓

Activity 9.1 Case Study: Understanding Supportive Communication

Purpose: To learn to apply the concepts of supportive communication climate and confirmation.

Instructions
1. This activity can be done individually, with a partner, or with a larger study group or class.
2. Review the case study of Imran that is presented below.
3. After you have read the story, answer the questions below.
4. Discuss your answers with a partner or study group.
5. How were your answers the same or different?

Example
When you are talking with your best friend, you feel very positive and confident. You know that there is something special about the relationship and the way that you talk to each other that produces this type of positive environment for you. You realize that you always receive a lovely, warm smile when you go to her house (recognition). You also know that she listens and focuses on you when you talk with her. She is not distracted, which you know because she always responds to you with interesting thoughts and enthusiasm (acknowledgement). The best part is that no matter what you do, even if you mess up, she will always support you with encouragement and enthusiasm (endorsement).

Case Study
Rick heads into a local coffee shop, so Imran, realizing that he must have agreed to go for a coffee with Rick, follows him. Deciding that he has nothing to lose, Imran follows Rick to a table in the corner. As they sit down, Rick starts to ask him some questions.

Rick: "Imran, you seemed kind of preoccupied while we were talking. Is everything okay with you?"

Imran: "Yeah, Rick, I'm sorry about that. I've had a lot of things on my mind. I am thinking about my work, and I am starting to question my next step."

Rick: "So, you are starting to think about where you are going in your career, and you are feeling anxious about that, huh?"

Imran: "I just am starting to wonder where my future lies and what I should be doing. I am even beginning to think about whether I should go back to school so that I can get a higher level of degree."

Rick: (He nods.) "I can understand how you would feel stressed thinking about something like that."

Imran: "All of my life I have known what I was going to do, and all of a sudden, I feel uncertain."

Rick: "You have always been a focused guy, Imran, and I have admired your ability to always go forward with your life and with a direction."

Imran: "Thanks, Rick. I appreciate your saying that about me. I have always admired your laid-back attitude. You never seem to get stressed."

Rick: "Oh, I get stressed all right. I think that I am just good at hiding it from people."

Imran: "Really? So it sounds like you don't like sharing that part of yourself with people, eh?"

Rick: "I've had some bad experiences with telling people how I feel, so I generally try to hold it in."

Imran: "I can understand that. It sounds as though you have learned that not all people are to be trusted. That makes sense to me."

What levels of confirmation and disconfirmation did you see in this exchange? What messages were communicated with these? Provide examples:

Level of Confirmation/Disconfirmation:

Example(s):

Level of Confirmation/Disconfirmation:

Example(s):

Level of Confirmation/Disconfirmation:

Example(s):

Activity 9.2 Features of Relationships

Purposes: To allow you to apply research on close relationships to two important relationships in your life. To help you understand the bases of satisfaction in two important relationships in your life.

Instructions
1. To refresh your knowledge of the four features that research indicates characterize satisfying close relationships, read "Features of Satisfying Personal Relationships" in the textbook (p. 251).
2. Identify a close friend and a current or past romantic partner, each of whom you did or do have a satisfying close relationship with.
3. Use forms A and B on the following pages to describe central features of satisfying relationships as they operate in your life.

Example
As you reflect on your best friend you think about how long you have been friends and all that you have been through together. You can tell him anything, and you know that he will never tell anyone your secrets. You have plans to travel to Europe together next summer, and you are really excited about the trip. You know that you two will travel well together as you both tend to like the same things and feel the same way about the need for independence while travelling. You know that you will spend most days together but that there may be times when you do your own thing based upon what you want to do for the day.

Investment: You have been friends for a long time—that is investment.

Commitment: You have made plans to do something together in the future, your Europe trip.

Trust: You can tell him anything and know that he will never tell anyone; you trust him.

Relational Dialectics: You manage your degree of closeness with acceptance that you will each need time to yourselves, and you are both comfortable with this.

FORM A: FEATURES IN FRIENDSHIP

Feature
Presence in Your
Relationship

1. Investments
   * What have you invested?

   * What has your friend invested?

2. Commitment
   *   How certain are you that the two of
       you will remain close friends?

   *   To what extent do the two of you talk
       about a shared future or future plans?

3. Trust
   *   How much do you feel you can rely on your
       friend to do what she or he says she or he
       will do?

   *   How much do you count on your friend to look
       out for you and your welfare?

4. Relational Dialectics

   *   How do you manage needs for autonomy
       and connection?

   *   How do you manage needs for novelty and
       predictability?

   *   How do you manage needs for openness
       and privacy?

FORM B: FEATURES IN ROMANTIC RELATIONSHIP

Feature	Presence in Your Relationship

1. Investments
   * What have you invested?

   * What has your partner invested?

2. Commitment
   * How certain are you that the two of you will remain together in a romantic relationship?

   * To what extent do the two of you talk about a shared future or future plans?

3. Trust
   * How much do you feel you can rely on your partner to do what she or he says she or he will do?

   * How much do you count on your partner to look out for you and your welfare?

4. Relational Dialectics

   * How do you manage needs for autonomy and connection?

   * How do you manage needs for novelty and predictability?

   * How do you manage needs for openness and privacy?

Activity 9.3 Increasing Your Awareness of Self-Disclosure Risk Levels

Purpose: To provide you with an opportunity to compare your perception of the risk level involved with different types of self-disclosure and to compare that with the perceptions of others in your class. Knowing how others feel about the appropriateness of disclosing certain types of information will help you in making appropriate choices when self-disclosing or receiving disclosures from others.

Instructions
1. This activity can be done individually, with a partner, or with a larger study group or class.
2. Follow the instructions below with regard to rating your own comfort with self-disclosure.
3. Compare your list with those of classmates, including at least one person from a different culture.
4. What are the differences in levels of comfort with regard to self-disclosure?

Complete the following list of statements according to how you perceive its risk (L = Low risk; M = Moderate risk; H = High risk).

_____1. Your parents' marital status

_____2. Your academic major

_____3. Your grades

_____4. Your religious affiliation and beliefs

_____5. Your marital or dating status

_____6. Your political affiliation and views

_____7. The details of your sex life

_____8. Your weakness that you most detest

_____9. Your strength that you most like

_____10. Your hopes and dreams for the future

_____11. Your biggest disappointments in the past

_____12. Your own dependencies or vices

_____13. Your biggest accomplishment

_____14. Your biggest failure

Activity 9.4 Distinguishing Aggressive, Assertive, and Deferential Forms of Communication

Purpose: To increase your awareness of distinctions among aggressive, assertive, and deferential styles of communicating.

Instructions
Listed below are five scenarios that describe a situation and your goal in the situation. For each scenario, write an aggressive, assertive, and deferential statement expressing your goal.

Example

Scenario:	You need to study for an examination, but your boyfriend/girlfriend really wants to go out for dinner and a movie.
Aggressive response:	"I don't care about your preferences. I'm not going out tonight."
Assertive response:	"I'd like to go out tomorrow or this weekend, but I have to study tonight."
Deferential response:	"I guess studying isn't really that important. We can go out if you want to."

Scenario 1:	You think your roommate is angry with you, but you have no idea why. He or she denied being angry when you stated your perception. But he or she is acting very distant and unfriendly.

Aggressive response:

Assertive response:

Deferential response:

Scenario 2:   One of your close friends asks to borrow your car. Normally, you wouldn't mind lending
                your car to a friend, but this person has a record of speeding and being careless behind the
                wheel. You can't afford to have your car wrecked.

  Aggressive response:

  Assertive response:

  Deferential response:

Scenario 3:   A close friend asks you about something very personal. You want to show that you trust
                the friend, but you don't want to discuss this topic—even with a close friend.

  Aggressive response:

  Assertive response:

  Deferential response:

Scenario 4:   Ten days ago you loaned $20 to one of your coworkers with the understanding that the loan would be repaid within a week. The coworker has not repaid the money nor offered any explanation. You need the loan repaid.

Aggressive response:

Assertive response:

Deferential response:

Scenario 5:   One of the people in a group to which you belong tells racist and sexist jokes. You find the jokes very offensive, but you don't want to create tension in the group or make the person who tells the jokes feel bad. You just want the jokes to stop.

Aggressive response:

Assertive response:

Deferential response:

Activity 9.5 Rating the Supportiveness of Communication Climates

Purposes: To provide you with experience in identifying communication that tends to foster defensive and supportive climates between people. To demonstrate the practical value of knowledge about supportive and defence-producing styles of communicating.

Instructions

1. This exercise can be done individually, with a partner, or with a larger group or class. It can also be done online with individuals communicating at a distance.
2. If you do not have a clear memory of the kinds of communication that cultivate defensive and supportive communication climates, reread "Defensive and Supportive Climates" in your textbook (p. 264).
3. Identify two TV shows that you can all observe online. One show should demonstrate a relationship that has a supportive climate in which partners seem to feel safe, at ease, and supported by each other. The second should demonstrate a relationship in which a defensive climate prevails—partners should seem to feel on guard and unsure of each other's motives and support.
4. Use form A below to identify examples of communication that is linked to defensive and supportive climates in the relationship that has a supportive climate. Try to record each example of supportive and defence-producing communication.
5. Use form B below to identify examples of communication that is linked to defensive and supportive climates in the relationship that has a defensive climate. Try to record each example of supportive and defence-producing communication.
6. Compare the profiles of communication for the two relationships.

FORM A

**USE TO CODE COMMUNICATION IN A RELATIONSHIP
THAT HAS A *SUPPORTIVE* CLIMATE**

Communication Type	Number of Instances Observed

Evaluation

_____

Description

_____

Certainty

_____

Provisionalism

_____

Strategy

_____

Spontaneity

_____

Control-orientation

_____

Problem-orientation

_____

Neutrality

_____

Empathy

_____

Superiority

_____

Equality

_____

FORM B

**USE TO CODE COMMUNICATION IN A RELATIONSHIP
THAT HAS A *DEFENSIVE* CLIMATE**

Communication Type	Number of Instances Observed
Evaluation	
Description	
Certainty	
Provisionalism	
Strategy	
Spontaneity	
Control-orientation	
Problem-orientation	
Neutrality	
Empathy	
Superiority	
Equality	

Chapter 10: Managing Conflict in Relationships

I. <u>Conflict</u> exists when individuals who depend upon each other express different views, interests, or goals, and perceive them as incompatible or oppositional.

    A. Conflict must be recognized and/or expressed. I often express conflict verbally by saying

        _____ ;

        I often express conflict nonverbally by _____

        _____ .

    B. All parties involved in the conflict must depend upon each other.

    C. Conflict arises when we perceive that there are incompatible goals, preferences, or decisions that must be resolved to maintain the relationship.

II. There are basic principles of conflict.

    A. Conflict is a natural part of our relationships that indicates the people involved are connected to each other.

    B. Conflict may be open, explicit, or overt, or it may be hidden, implicit, or covert. An example of overt conflict in my life is _____ .

        1. <u>Passive aggression,</u> a common form of covert conflict, occurs when individuals act aggressively but deny the aggressive behaviour. An example of covert conflict in my life is _____ .

        2. Covert conflict often happens through <u>games</u> in which real conflicts are hidden or denied.

C. Our responses to conflict can benefit or harm us and the relationship in which we are involved. An example of a time when conflict benefited one of my relationships is

_____ ;

an example of a time when conflict harmed one of my relationships is _____

_____ .

III. Social influences (cultural background, gender, and sexual orientation) affect our orientation toward and responses to conflict.

IV. How conflicts are managed directly influences the future of the relationship.

V. Handling conflict in constructive ways can promote personal and relational growth.

VI. There are three basic orientations people have toward conflict.

A. A lose–lose approach assumes that expressing conflict is unhealthy for everyone involved in the relationship. This approach works well when we are trying to figure out if we need to engage in conflict, especially if the issue is less important than others. An example of a lose–lose orientation that I have seen is _____

_____ .

B. A win–lose approach assumes that expressing conflict leads to one person benefiting and the other person not achieving a desired outcome. This approach works well when we have low commitment to the relationship and/or a small desire to exert the energy necessary to engage in conflict. An example of a win–lose orientation that I have seen is

_____

_____ .

C. A win–win approach assumes that expressing conflict leads to all people involved working together to come up with a solution that is acceptable to everyone. An example of a win–win orientation that I have seen is _____

_____ .

VII.   Most people have relatively consistent patterns they employ to respond to conflict.

    A.   We use <u>exit responses</u> when we leave the relationship, either physically or psychologically. Exit responses are most consistent with _____ orientations.

    B.   We use <u>neglect responses</u> when we minimize or deny the conflict exists. Neglect responses are most consistent with _____ and _____ orientations.

    C.   We use <u>loyalty responses</u> when we remain committed to continuing the relationship and choose to put up with the differences. Loyalty responses are most consistent with _____ orientations.

    D.   We use <u>voice responses</u> when we actively seek to talk openly about and resolve the conflict. Voice responses are most consistent with _____ orientations.

VIII.   The communication pattern we choose during conflict can help or hinder the relationship.

    A.   Ineffective communication damages efforts to resolve the conflict, harms individuals, and jeopardizes relational health.

        1.   Early in the process, we use communication that disconfirms the other person.

        2.   Once a negative climate has been established, we maintain it by engaging in additional negative communication (e.g., frequent interruptions).

        3.   In the later stages of the conflict, all parties feel the pressure to resolve the conflict, usually on their own terms rather than taking the other person's proposals into account.

    B.   Constructive communication is open, nonjudgmental, confirming, and non-strategic.

        1.   Prior to the conflict, people confirm each other by recognizing and acknowledging each other's concerns and feelings; when the conflict arises, they know that they are both working together to come up with a solution.

        2.   In the middle stages, everyone focuses on the specific issues at hand and eliminates all potential distractions, including previous conflicts.

3.   In the final resolution stages, both partners work to take parts of each proposal put on the table to agree upon a solution everyone can accept.

IX.   Several skills are identified that are essential for effective conflict management: attending to the relationship level of meaning; communicating supportively; listening mindfully; taking responsibility for your thoughts, feelings, and issues; checking perceptions; looking for points of agreement; looking for ways to preserve the other person's face; and imagining how you will feel in the future.

X.   There are at least five guidelines for improving conflict communication.

A.   We need to focus on the entire system in which communication occurs rather than just on the conflict or disagreement. An example of a time when I should have considered the whole system is _____.

B.   We need to pay attention to the timing of conflicts: chronemics (make sure all parties are completely present mentally, be flexible about when to handle conflict, and set aside tangential issues for another time). An example of a time when I should have paid more attention to timing is _____.

C.   If we care about the other person and our relationship, we should aim for a win–win approach. An example of a time when I should have striven for a win–win resolution is

_____.

D.   Honour and respect yourself as well as the other person/people involved and the relationship. An example of a time when I should have honoured and respected everyone involved in the conflict is _____.

E.   Consider whether it is appropriate to put aside our own needs if there is no rule or standard that says we should grant the other compassion. An example of a time when I should have exhibited grace is _____.

Activities

Title	Individual	Partner	Group	Ethno	Internet InfoTrac
10.1 Understanding How Conflict Happens	✓	✓	✓	✓	
10.2 Understanding Cultural Differences about Conflict	✓	✓	✓	✓	✓
10.3 Generating Different Responses to Conflict	✓	✓	✓		
10.4 Identifying Orientations to Conflict	✓	✓	✓		
10.5 Understanding Your Conflict Script	✓				

Activity 10.1 Understanding How Conflict Happens

Purpose: To learn to apply the concepts of understanding conflict.

Instructions
1.   This activity can be done individually, with a partner, or with a larger study group or class. You can also post the story online for an online discussion.
2.   Review the case study of Imran that is presented below.
3.   After you have read the story, answer the questions on the next page.
4.   Discuss your answers with a partner or study group.
5.   How were your answers the same or different?

Example

When you fight with someone in your life, there are certain patterns that you may be aware of in the conflict. For instance, you may find yourself using a win–lose orientation, which means that you think that one person is always going to win and one person is always going to lose. This type of orientation affects the way that the conflict unfolds.

Case Study

Imran says goodbye to Rick and proceeds on his way to the office. As he walks along the street, he finds himself walking behind a teenager and a person who appears to be the boy's father. Their voices are raised, so Imran can't help but overhear the conversation that takes place. They appear to be arguing about the son attending his grandmother's birthday party. The boy wants to go to a concert, and his father wants him to go to the birthday celebration. Imran hears the father say, "I am sure we can find some way to figure this out," but the boy does not seem to hear him. He is yelling at his father, "I never get to do things I want; it is always you who makes the decisions!" The boy proceeds to yell at his father and tell him what a horrible father he is and how much he hates him. Imran finds it increasingly uncomfortable to listen as the boy's anger escalates. He starts thinking about his own relationship with his father and the discussion they had the night before. Imran marvels at the differences between his response to discomfort and the teenage boy's response to discomfort. Imran would never challenge his father in the manner that this boy is doing. In his family, the children were expected to respect the voice of the elders no matter what the situation. The youth were not allowed to talk back to their elders but instead maintain a respectful silence. His thoughts are broken by the sudden loud scream by the teenage boy, who runs by him yelling back at his father, "I hate you! Go away!"

Questions for Discussion and Review

What were the orientations to conflict in the case study?

What were the responses to conflict?

What signs of unproductive communication did you observe?

What strategies could be used to make this a more productive conflict?

Activity 10.2 Understanding Cultural Differences about Conflict

Purpose: To gain an understanding of how different cultures manage conflict in their communities.

Instructions
1.   Gather a group of five people, either face-to-face or online. If possible, each of the five people should represent a different culture. Try to ensure that you also have a mixed gender group.
2.   Each person is to review and answer the list of questions below.
3.   If all individuals in the group are from the same culture, use the Internet as a tool to find information about the norms of different cultures with regard to conflict.
4.   Discuss the different culture norms regarding conflict.

Example
As stated in the text, the majority of Mediterranean cultures regard conflict as both normal and a valuable part of everyday life. How is that different from your own cultural norms of expressing conflict?

Questions

Is conflict considered a normal part of everyday life in my culture?

Is everyone free to express his or her views, or is this right restricted to specific members of the culture (i.e., men)?

How do members of my culture express the following emotions both verbally and nonverbally?

➤ Anger

➤ Sadness

➤ Disappointment

➤ Fear

➢ Disgust

➢ Confusion

Do you see these values changing as a result of immigration and cultural assimilation?

Activity 10.3 Generating Different Responses to Conflict

Purposes: To give you practice in generating communication that reflects each of the four responses to interpersonal conflict. To increase your repertoire of methods for responding to interpersonal conflict.

Instructions

1. This activity can be done individually, with a partner, or with a larger study group.
2. If you do not recall the textbook's discussion of different responses to conflict, review "Responses to Conflict" in the textbook (p. 290).
3. Listed below are five conflict scenarios. For each one, write four responses—one each that reflects exit, voice, loyalty, and neglect responses.

Scenario 1

The person you have been dating suggests that it's time the two of you talked about commitment. You feel unready to discuss a serious relationship, but your partner insists that she or he thinks the two of you need to talk about it.

Exit response:

Voice response:

Loyalty response:

Neglect response:

Scenario 2

One of your friends brings up a political race, and you make a comment about the strengths of the candidate you support. Your friend says, "I can't believe you support that jerk. What has he done for the environment?"

Exit response:

Voice response:

Loyalty response:

Neglect response:

Scenario 3

One of your coworkers continuously misses deadlines in turning in reports to you. Since your reports require information from the coworker's reports, your reports also are routinely late. You don't want your late reports to interfere with your raises and advancement. You'd like for the coworker to be more prompt.

Exit response:

Voice response:

Loyalty response:

Neglect response:

Scenario 4

You tell your parents you'd like to take a term off from school. They are strongly opposed to the idea and tell you to stay in school.

Exit response:

Voice response:

Loyalty response:

Neglect response:

Scenario 5

You and your friend generally get together to watch the playoffs at his apartment. This year, your friend suggests that the two of you go downtown to one of the bars with a giant screen. Where you watch doesn't really matter to you.

Exit response:

Voice response:

Loyalty response:

Neglect response:

Activity 10.4 Identifying Orientations to Conflict

Purpose: To give you practice in recognizing orientations to conflict in concrete situations.

Instructions
1. This exercise can be done with a partner or with a larger study group.
2. For each of the statements listed below, indicate which orientation to conflict is most clearly reflected.
3. Use the letters below to indicate the corresponding orientations to conflict.
4. Correct answers appear at the end of the study guide chapter.
5. Discuss your responses with your partner or group members.

A.   win–lose

B.   lose–lose

C.   win–win

_____1.   We can't both be satisfied with a resolution to this problem.

_____2.   Since we disagree on where to go for our vacation, let's just not go anywhere.

_____3.   We are never going to see eye to eye on this. I think my preference should prevail.

_____4.   I think if we keep talking, we will figure out something that both of us can live with.

_____5.   I can't stand fighting. Everyone loses.

_____6.   No matter what you say, I'm not giving any ground on this issue. I feel very strongly, and I expect you to go along with me this time.

_____7.   There's no point in arguing about money. All we ever do is hurt each other without solving anything.

_____8.   I'm willing to go along with your preference on the model of car if you'll go along with my preference for colour and added features.

_____9.   Look: There are only two possibilities in this situation, so both of us can't get what we want.

_____10.   I wonder if there aren't some solutions other than the two we have come up with so far. I think if we keep talking, we might be able to come up with something workable for both of us.

Activity 10.5 Understanding Your Conflict Script

Purposes: To help you recognize ways in which your family shaped your views of conflict. To invite you to reconsider any unproductive conflict scripts that you learned.

Instructions

1. Respond to the questions below.
2. To summarize your responses to the questions, create a written description of the conflict script you learned in your family.
3. Identify any aspects of your conflict script that you would like to change.
4. Indicate strategies you will follow for revising aspects of your conflict script that you do not want to retain.

Did you ever witness your parents engaging in conflict?

If so, how often did they adopt win–win, win–lose, and lose–lose orientations toward conflict?

How often did each of your (step) parents rely on exit, voice, loyalty, and neglect responses to conflict?

A. Father

B. Mother

C. Stepfather

D. Stepmother

Do you recall any explicit statements about conflict that your parents made? For example, some parents tell children "conflict is bad" or "conflict is healthy." What do you recall hearing from your (step) parents?

What happened when conflict occurred in your family?

    A. Did individuals demonstrate respect for one another and one another's views?

    B. Was there any residual anger or negative feeling following conflicts?

    C. Did your parents try to get others to take sides?

Write the conflict script that you were taught in your family.

Identify any aspects of the conflict script you learned in your family that you would like to revise or
eliminate from your own views of conflict. For each aspect of your conflict script that you would like to
revise, indicate two specific strategies you might follow to create the desired change.

Desired Change in Script	Strategies for Changing
Example	
I want to change what I learned about trying to win in every case.	a. I will monitor my inclination to try to win just for the sake of winning.
	b. I will paraphrase other people's views to encourage myself to consider what they think and feel.
1.	a.
	b.
2.	a.
	b.
3.	a.
	b.

Answers to Activity 10.4 Identifying Orientations to Conflict

1. A

2. B

3. A

4. C

5. B

6. A

7. B

8. C

9. A

10. C

Chapter 11: Friendships and Romantic Relationships

I. Committed romantic relationships are voluntary, involve I–Thou communication, include sexual and romantic feelings, and are considered primary and permanent in our society.

   A. Our traditional definition of two heterosexual parents and children has evolved to include a variety of romantic relationship configurations both in Canada and around the world.

   B. Generally, romantic love involves passion (intensely positive feelings and desires for another person), commitment (an intention to remain in the relationship), and intimacy (feelings of connection, closeness, and tenderness).

   C. Romantic relationships develop based upon the love styles the partners exhibit.

      1. There are three primary love styles.

         a. <u>Eros</u> is an intense love that usually includes early self-disclosure, sentimental expressions, and a quick falling-in-love period.

         b. <u>Storge</u> love grows out of friendship and is usually characterized by stability.

         c. Those who exhibit a <u>ludus</u> style view love as a game that usually includes adventure, puzzles, and commitment avoidance.

      2. There are three secondary love styles.

         a. <u>Pragma</u> combines storge and ludus love styles; people who exhibit this love style usually have clear criteria for partners that must be met before they fall in love.

         b. <u>Mania</u> combines eros and ludus love styles; people who exhibit this love style usually devise games and tests for their potential partners and experience emotional extremes.

         c. <u>Agape</u> combines eros and storge love styles; people who exhibit this love style usually put another's happiness ahead of their own without any expectation of reciprocity.

II.	Like friendships, romantic relationships in Western societies tend to follow a relatively predictable path.

   A.	<u>Growth</u> stages begin a romantic relationship.

      1.	We are <u>individuals</u> before we ever meet our potential romantic partner.

      2.	<u>Invitational communication</u> is where we indicate to the other person that we are interested in interacting. One way I indicate interest is _____ _____.

      3.	<u>Explorational communication</u> involves considering the possibilities for a long- term relationship. One way I explore in a committed romantic relationship is _____ _____.

      4.	<u>Intensifying communication</u> occurs when we express more personal thoughts and feelings as well as begin to create our own relational culture. At this point in a committed romantic relationship, I usually express _____ _____.

      5.	<u>Revising communication</u> indicates the possible problems and dissatisfactions that exist within the relationship as well as evaluates the likelihood of the relationship continuing.

      6.	<u>Commitment</u> involves people's decision to stay with the relationship over the long haul and arrange other aspects of their lives around this relationship. I have expressed commitment in a romantic relationship by _____ _____.

   B.	<u>Navigation</u> maintains a relationship by adjusting, working through new problems, revisiting old problems, and accommodating changes in both individual and relational lives.

      1.	<u>Relational culture</u> is the private world of rules, understandings, meanings, and patterns of acting and interpreting that partners create and agree upon for their relationship.

Examples of relational culture I have experienced or witnessed are _____

_____

and _____.

2.   In <u>placemaking</u>, we create an environment that indicates our relationship as well as what we value, experience, and like. An example of placemaking I have experienced or witnessed is _____

_____.

C.   Deterioration stages signal a possible end to a romantic relationship.

1.   In the <u>intrapsychic phase</u>, we focus on perceived declines in closeness/intimate communication or lapses in joint activities/acts of consideration.

2.   <u>Dyadic breakdown</u> occurs when romantic partners gradually stop engaging in their established patterns, understandings, and routines that make up their relational culture.

3.   <u>Social support</u> occurs when we look to others to help us get through the relationship's breakdown. For social support I would turn to _____

_____.

4.   <u>Grave dressing</u> is burying the relationship and accepting that it has come to a close.

5.   <u>Resurrection</u> process occurs when both partners go on with their lives without the other as an intimate.

III.   Like all relationships, there are various things that make friendships difficult to develop and maintain.

A.   <u>Internal tensions</u> are relationship stressors that grow out of the individuals involved in the relationship.

1.   Relational dialectics (autonomy/connection, openness/privacy, and novelty/familiarity) create tension when the people involved in the friendship have different expectations and/or needs. An example of a time when relational dialectics created tension in one of my friendships is _____

_____.

2.   Social diversity creates tension when our interpretations of different communication styles or perceptions create misunderstandings. An example of a time when I saw social diversity

create tension in a friendship is _____

_____.

3. Sexual attraction creates tension when two friends have agreed not to add romance to their relationship or if one person wants romance and the other does not. An example of a time when I saw sexual attraction create tension in a friendship is _____

_____.

B. External tensions are relationship stressors that grow out of the situation or context surrounding the relationship.

1. Because our lives are complex and friendships have no rules governing how often, when, and where we interact, they are frequently the easiest relationship to neglect when we have too much to do. An example of a time when I had to meet too many demands to give a friendship the time it deserved is_____

_____.

2. Our friendships change as we make changes in our lives (e.g., starting a new educational stage, a new career, a family; caring for others). An example of a change that affected a friendship of mine is _____

_____.

3. Geographic distance is becoming a larger constraint as we become a more mobile society. An example of a friendship that was affected by geographic distance is _____

_____.

IV. Communicating in committed, healthy, romantic relationships requires an understanding of four guidelines.

A. Engaging in <u>dual perspective</u> lets your partner know that you understand his or her perspective and that you take it into consideration when communicating.

B. With the rise of HIV/AIDS comes the responsibility of talking about and <u>practising safer sex</u>, two things we are not always comfortable talking about or doing.

C. Manage conflict constructively as violence and abuse among romantic partners are, unfortunately, more common than we think.

D. Adapt communication to the unique needs of partners in commuter relationships.

Activities

Title	Individual	Partner	Group	Ethno	Internet InfoTrac
11.1 Case Study: Dimensions of Close Relationships	✓	✓	✓	✓	
11.2 Online Friendships	✓	✓	✓	✓	✓
11.3 Recognizing Styles of Love	✓	✓	✓		
11.4 Identifying Stages in Romantic Relationships	✓	✓	✓		
11.5 Relational Dialectics in Your Romantic Relationship	✓				

Activity 11.1 Case Study: Dimensions of Close Relationships

Purpose: To learn to apply the concepts of understanding conflict.

Instructions

1.   This activity can be done individually, with a partner, or with a larger study group or class. You can also post the story online for an online discussion.
2.   Review the case study of Imran that is presented below.
3.   After you have read the story, answer the question below.
4.   Discuss your answers with a partner or study group.
5.   How were your answers the same or different?

Case Study

As Imran proceeds toward work, his cellphone rings. He looks down to see that it is his friend Garcia calling. He realizes that he has not talked to Garcia in a long time and happily answers the call. Imran has known Garcia all of his life—the two grew up together on the same street, attended the same schools all of their lives, and shared many happy memories. They were both on the debating team at school, and they used to spend many hours discussing political issues in the country. The school they attended was a very sports-oriented school, and Garcia was one of the few people who seemed to understand the challenges of being a first-generation Canadian and having parents who were immigrants. When his parents gave him a hard time, Imran would call Garcia, knowing that he could tell him how he felt and that he wouldn't tell anyone what he said. He also knew that Garcia would help him find a solution to any struggles he was having, no matter how big or small.

Question

How does Imran's relationship with Garcia reflect the dimensions of close relationships?

➤   Willingness to invest

➤   Emotional closeness

➤   Acceptance

➤   Trust

➤   Support

Activity 11.2 Online Friendships

Purpose: To understand the differences between methods of staying connected to significant people in your life.

Instructions

1. This activity can be done individually, with a partner, or with a larger study group or class. It can also be posted online for online discussion.
2. Identify one person who you primarily stay connected with using each of the methods listed below.
3. What are the benefits of the chosen method?
4. What are the drawbacks of the method?
5. Post a question on your social network site and ask your peers and friends what method they most prefer to use.
6. Ask someone who is of an older generation than you how they stay connected to their friends.
7. Ask someone who is a recent immigrant to Canada how he or she stays connected with friends and family living in another country.
8. Discuss your findings with your study group.

Example

You have a friend who lives in the United States. You use the telephone as a primary means of staying connected with her. You have another friend who lives in the same city as you, and you use a social networking site to stay connected. What differences do you notice in the different methods that you use?

Method	Benefits	Drawbacks
The telephone		
E-mail		
Texting		

Method	Benefits	Drawbacks
Social networking site		
Web cam		

How do methods of keeping in touch differ among various generations?

How are they different among various cultures?

Activity 11.3 Recognizing Styles of Love

Purpose: To give you experience in identifying communication that reflects particular styles of loving.

Instructions

1. This activity can be done individually, with a partner, or with a larger study group or class. It can also be posted online for an online discussion.
2. Listed below are 15 statements that might be made by a person about romance or a romantic partner. Identify the style of love reflected in each of the statements (eros, storge, ludus, pragma, mania, agape).
3. Answers appear at the end of the study guide chapter.

Style of Love	Statement
Example	
Agape	Your happiness is my happiness.
_____1.	I want to tell my partner everything about me as soon as I fall in love.
_____2.	My partner is my best friend.
_____3.	I could fall in love with only someone of my race and class.
_____4.	I am looking for a partner who will be a good parent.
_____5.	Love's a game—I never take it too seriously.
_____6.	I wish I could be sure Pat loves me. I worry all the time.
_____7.	I put Kim's welfare and desires ahead of my own, and that's the way I want it to be.
_____8.	I fall in love hard and fast.
_____9.	I am not looking for a committed relationship, just some fun.

_____10. All I can think about is this relationship. Nothing and nobody else matters to me.

_____11. I am happiest when my partner is happy.

_____12. What I like best about my relationship is that it is so steady and peaceful—none of those dramatic ups and downs that some couples have.

_____13. I need to make sure my partner loves me, so I come up with tests a lot of the time.

_____14. I intend to marry someone who is professionally ambitious.

_____15. Our love just grew very gradually. We started off as friends, and eventually romantic interest developed an extra layer on the basic foundation of friendship.

Activity 11.4 Identifying Stages in Romantic Relationships

Purpose: To give you experience in identifying communication that reflects different stages in the evolution of romantic relationships.

Instructions

1. This activity can be done individually, with a partner, or with a larger study group or class. It can also be posted online for an online discussion.
2. Listed below are 12 interactions between partners A and B that would most likely occur at specific stages in a romantic relationship.
3. Identify the stage of romance most clearly reflected in each of the interactions.
4. Answers appear at the end of the chapter study guide.

Stage	Interaction between Partners
Example	
Revising	A: Before I could consider a permanent relationship, you would need to stop smoking. B: I understand that condition.
1. _____	A: Where are you from? B: Ohio. Where is your home?
2. _____	A: I plan to spend the rest of my life with you. B: I feel the same way.
3. _____	A: (thought, not stated) I'm just not happy in this relationship. We don't communicate anymore. B: (thought not stated) I really miss doing things together.
4. _____	A: Do you enjoy bands like this one? B: Sure, but I like jazz even more. Do you like jazz?
5. _____	A: I think I finally understand what went wrong in our relationship and why we couldn't make it work. B: Me too, so now we can let it go.

6. _____

A: It's so comfortable to have established routines and understandings in our relationship

B: Yeah, there's a nice basic rhythm in our lives together.

7. _____

A: I just called to say good night. Even though we spent four hours talking tonight, I wanted to talk to you once more before going to sleep.

B: I'm glad you called. I can't get enough of you.

8. _____

A: (unstated realization) We don't ask about each other's day anymore like we used to do all the time.

B: (unstated realization) We used to go out for brunch every Sunday, but we don't anymore.

9. _____

A: (to parent) It's over between Pat and me, and I'm really sad.

B: (to friend) Kim and I just broke up, and I'm kind of down.

10. _____

A: I know that I love you, but I'm not sure we can make a permanent life together.

B: Why not? Let's talk about your questions and see if we can find answers to them. I want to make this work.

11. _____

A: How are we going to tell our parents we're separating? There's never been a divorce in either of our families.

B: I know. I think it's really important that neither of us blame each other when we talk to our families. Will you agree to that?

Activity 11.5 Relational Dialectics in Your Romantic Relationship

Purposes: To heighten your awareness of the presence of relational dialectics in an important current or past romantic relationship in your life. To give you insight into the normalcy and health of opposing needs in a current or past romantic relationship in which you are or have been involved.

Instructions

1. This activity can be done individually, with a partner, or with a larger study group or class. It can also be posted online for an online discussion.
2. Identify an important current or past romantic relationship in your life. Use that relationship as the referent for filling in the chart below. Provide an example of each pole of the three relational dialectics.
3. Identify what would be lost if the example you identified was not in your romantic relationship.

Dialectic	Specific Example in Your Relationship	What Would Be Lost If This Were Not Present
Example		
Autonomy	I spend most weekends in a private retreat so that I can write without interference.	I would be unhappy if I did not have time to write. I would not appreciate time with Robbie as much if it were routine.

A. Autonomy/Connectedness

   A-1: Autonomy

   A-2: Connectedness

Dialectic	Specific Example in Your Relationship	What Would Be Lost If This Were Not Present

B. Novelty/Predicatability

    B-1: Novelty

    B-2: Predictability

C. Openness/Closedness

    C-1: Openness

    C-2: Closedness

Answers to Activity 11.3 Recognizing Styles of Love

1.   Eros

2.   Storge

3.   Pragma

4.   Pragma

5.   Ludus

6.   Mania

7.   Agape

8.   Eros

9.   Ludus

10.   Mania

11.   Agape

12.   Storge

13.   Mania

14.   Pragma

15.   Storge

Answers to Activity 11.4 Identifying Stages in Romantic Relationships

1.   Invitational communication

2.   Commitment

3.   Intrapsychic phase

4.   Explorational communication

5.   Grave dressing

6.   Navigating

7.   Intensifying communication (euphoria)

8.   Dyadic processes

9.   Social support

10.   Revising communication

11.   Resurrection processes

Chapter 12: Relationships at Work

I.   Relationships in the workplace are unique. We have many different types of relationships with people at work. The people that I have enjoyed working with include _____

_____

_____

_____.

II.   Work relationships are not always equal. Power greatly influences our relationships with each other.

     A.   The type of power that has the ability to punish or withhold resources is known

         as_____.

     B.   The type of power that has the ability to reward is known as _____ power.

     C.   Someone who has special knowledge is known as _____.

     D.   Some people hold _____ power due to their position.

     E.   Knowing the right people is known as _____ power.

     F.   Some people have referent power; this is due to their _____.

III.   The communication climate of a workplace greatly affects a worker's satisfaction with his or her work.

     A.   Workers need to feel a sense of personal support from their workplace. A time that I have been supported in my workplace is _____

_____

_____.

     B.   Workers who feel that they can participate in the decision making of the organization feel more satisfied. How did (does) your organization allow you to participate in decisions that affect you?

_____

_____

_____.

C.   Workers' feeling that they can trust the people they work with influences the climate of the organization. Which people you have worked with do you feel you could trust?

_____

_____

_____.

D.   When coworkers and supervisors can be open with each other, the climate at work is more positive. How have you seen people being open with each other at work?

_____

_____

_____.

E.   When employees can obtain goals, they have a higher degree of job satisfaction. What types of goals have you wanted to achieve at work? Were you successful?

_____

_____

_____.

IV.   The organizational culture refers to the overall pattern of belief, values, and practices that are evident in an organization.

A.   The values of an organization that are important to me include _____

_____

_____

_____.

B.   How does an organization reflect these values through vocabulary, rites, and rituals?

_____

_____

_____

V.   Group work is an important part of working in organizations.

A.   Teams involve interaction, interdependence, shared rules, and common goals.

B.   Groups have the potential to think through issues more thoroughly, bring heightened creativity, and often provide enhanced commitment to decisions.

C.   Groups can also slow down decision making and lead to increased pressure to conform if there are tight deadlines.

D.   My own experience with groups at a workplace has been _____

_____

_____

_____.

VI.   Communication within groups is one of the most essential components of effective group work.

A.   The type of communication that focuses on problems, issues, or information is known as

_____ communication.

B.   The type of communication that helps a group get organized and stay on track in its decision making is known as _____ communication.

C.   _____ communication encourages people to contribute freely and evaluate ideas critically.

D.   A dysfunctional communication used to block others or call attention to oneself by devaluing another person's ideas is known as _____ communication.

VII.   One of the biggest challenges of the work environment can be our coworkers. How we manage the different personalities of our workplace can greatly affect not only our success at work but our overall enjoyment of our workplace.

A.   Procrastinators or perfectionists can miss deadlines because they believe that their work must be perfect. A solution to deal with this type of behaviour is _____

_____

_____.

B.   People who are verbally abusive violate others' rights. A technique to deal with someone who is verbally abusive would be to _____

_____

_____.

C.   Complainers and "yes but-ters" focus on the negative and are not committed to solving problems. An approach to dealing with this type of personality would be to _____

_____

_____.

D.   Egocentric self-summarizers constantly bring the issues and topics around to their own needs and do not use dual perspective. A solution to respond to this type of behaviour would include

_____

_____

_____.

E.   Noncommittal "I don't know" people are often afraid to voice their opinions. What is a possible response that you could make to this type of person?

_____

_____

_____.

F.   Sneaky, manipulative people are not straightforward with their ideas and are often looking to catch you off guard. A solution that I could try with this type of person would be _____

_____

_____

_____.

VIII.   There are several guidelines that individuals can follow to improve and maintain effective communication in the workplace.

A.   In order to participate effectively at work you must adhere to certain principles and guidelines. How are you going to maintain or change your behaviour in the following ways at work?

1.   I am going to demonstrate dual perspective by _____

_____

_____

_____.

2.   I am going to demonstrate mindful listening by _____

_____

_____

_____.

3. I am going to monitor my tendencies to damage work relationships by becoming more aware of these behaviours: _____

    _____

    _____

    _____.

4. I am going to demonstrate leadership skills at work by doing the following: _____

    _____

    _____

    _____.

Activities

Title	Individual	Partner	Group	Ethno	Internet InfoTrac
12.1 Working in an Organization	✓	✓	✓		
12.2 Understanding the Culture and Climate of Organizations	✓	✓	✓		✓
12.3 Family-Friendly Organizations	✓	✓	✓		✓
12.4 Understanding Power	✓	✓	✓	✓	
12.5 Working in a Group around Common Work Worries			✓		

Activity 12.1 Working in an Organization

Purpose: To apply the concepts from the theory to a practical case study example.

Instructions
1. This activity can be done individually, with a partner, or with a larger study group or class. It can also be posted online for an online discussion.
2. Review the case study of Imran that is presented below.
3. After you have read the story, answer the questions on the next page.
4. Discuss your answers with your partner or study group.
5. How were your answers the same or different?

Case Study

Just as he was walking into the office, Imran finished his telephone conversation. He feels very upbeat and is in a much better mood then he was when he woke this morning. He greets the office manager, Shelley, with a warm "Hello, how are you?" She responds with an equally warm welcome. He notices that there are flowers on her desk and that the waiting room is filled with many clients waiting for appointments. He does not worry about the clients because there are lots of interesting magazines as well as computers that the clients can use in the waiting room. They used to have a bleak, cold-looking waiting room, but a committee was struck last year to redesign the waiting room so that it was more comfortable for the company's clients. Imran thinks the chairs and couches certainly are a nice feature.

At his office cubicle, he greets the other people in his area. He likes most of them but does find one guy, Rob, difficult to work with. Imran had to work with him on a project team and struggled with finding ways to get along with him. Rob always missed deadlines but worked hard at convincing the bosses of what a wonderful worker he was. In particular, he always found a way to show off when the executive director, Jane, was around. In Jane's presence, Rob would pretend that he was the most interested in the project, but in reality, he sometimes fell asleep in meetings.

Imran puts down his coat and hurries to get ready for a department meeting. He does not want to be late, in part because Althea is going to be there and he wants to make a good impression on her. Although she is not the leader of this particular team, he knows that she will be watching him since a prospective promotion still looms. The leader of the group is Samuel. He is a very friendly man, and Imran can see why he is successful as a manager. He is easygoing—not the traditional sort of leader who makes everyone fearful—and always has nice personal things to say to the team members who work for him. Imran feels that he has learned a lot from working with Samuel. Somehow, his style of managing brings out the best in his employees, and everyone always wants to please him. Althea is a different type of manager. She has an impressive educational background and a wealth of knowledge. It is well known throughout the office that she is smart and thoughtful in her responses. Imran has another reason not to be late: he has a unique role on the team. As the team recorder of minutes, he is responsible for ensuring that the team stays on task. Imran heads off to the meeting feeling very upbeat and looking forward to the day.

Questions for Discussion and Reflection

What details did you notice that provide you with information about the climate of the organization?

What types of leadership was described in the case study?

Who was identified as a difficult person to work with? What characteristics would make him difficult to work with?

What could you do if you worked with someone like him?

What type of role did Imran play on his team?

Do you think that Imran is satisfied with his work environment?

Activity 12.2 Understanding the Culture and Climate of Organizations

Purpose: To increase your awareness of how organizations reflect and act on their values.

Instructions

1. This activity can be done individually, with a partner, or with a larger study group. It can also be posted online for discussion with colleagues who are at a distance.
2. Identify two organizations that you can compare.
3. If completing this with a study group, ask each person to identify one organization to focus on. Ideally, these should be organizations that you have some knowledge about from either having worked there or knowing someone who has.
4. Go to the website of the organization and answer the questions listed below.
5. Compare your answers with those of your colleagues.

Example

You work at a fast-food restaurant. The mission statement identifies that the key value of the organization is the people who work there. You reflect on your own experience working in the organization and struggle to see how the organization works to reflect this value in its day-to-day operations. Your own experience does not support the values that the company states it has. Why do you think this is?

Name of Organization:

Mission Statement/Vision Statement:

What is your interpretation of the mission statement?

What types of programs or services does the organization have available for its employees and their families?

How do these reflect the values of the organization?

How do these affect the climate of the organization?

Activity 12.3 Family-Friendly Organizations

Purpose: To gain an understanding of how organizations are working to become more family-friendly.

Instructions

1. This activity can be done individually, with a partner, or with a study group. It can also be posted online for discussion with colleagues who are at a distance.
2. Choose a Canadian search engine and type in "family-friendly organizations." You will be led to a site that lists Canada's top family-friendly employers.
3. Using the forms on the next page, review two organizations that are of interest to you.
4. Complete the checklist below of what they have to offer to their employees and their families.
5. Which organization most appeals to you?
6. Compare and discuss your choice of top family-friendly employer with your partner or study group.
7. What different reasons did you each have for selecting the organization that you did?

Example

You notice that the organization that you chose has a top-up on maternity leave benefits. You think that this reflects an important value of the organization: it respects the significance of families. This is important to you also because you hope to get pregnant this year, so you are more aware of the policies that organizations have with regard to this type of issue.

Organization 1

Benefit	What It Signifies to You

Organization 2

Benefit	What It Signifies to You

Activity 12.4 Understanding Power

Purposes: To gain an understanding of the different types of power that exist in organizations and how they affect the people who work there. To gain an understanding of how culture affects the perception of power.

Instructions

1. This activity can be done individually, with a partner, or with a study group. It can also be posted online for discussion with colleagues who are at a distance.
2. Review the list of the different types of power in the workplace on the next page.
3. Post an online survey about power using these terms.
4. Ask respondents to provide you with examples of the different types of power they have seen in the organizations they have worked for.
5. Identify the impact that this power has had on this person or other employees.
6. If possible, try to include two or more people from other cultures to gain a perspective on how our views of power are influenced by our cultural norms.
7. Answer the questions listed below with either a partner or a study group.

Questions

What do you think is the most effective type of power?

When would it be important to use different types of power?

Can people develop power? Why or why not?

Types of Power

Power	Influence on Employees	Cultural Variations/Interpretations
Coercive		
Reward		
Expert		
Legitimate		
Referent		
Networking		
Helplessness		

Activity 12.5 Working in a Group around Common Work Worries

Purposes: To gain an opportunity to experience working in a group method. To further understand how difficult personalities can affect the group process.

Instructions

1. Collect a group of six to eight people to work together.
2. Below is a list of common work worries. As a group, you are to classify what worry you think is the most significant or important.
3. The other items are to be ranked according to the degree of importance in the group.
4. Each of the people in the group is to assume one of the following group roles while completing this exercise :
   a. Procrastinator/perfectionist
   b. Verbally abusive person
   c. Complainer and "yes but-ter"
   d. Egocentric self-talk summarizer
   e. Noncommittal person
   f. Sneaky, manipulative person
5. Upon completion of the exercise, debrief with the questions listed on the following page.

Issues to Be Ranked

- Bad bosses
- Bullying
- Career management
- Difficult coworkers
- E-mail, Internet, and privacy
- Employee rights
- Harassment and discrimination
- Office politics and interpersonal relations
- Problem employees
- Reports and surveys
- Salaries and compensation
- Self-assessment and management

Debriefing Questions

How did you see the dynamics of the group operating?

How did each of the personalities affect the group process?

How did other people handle them?

Was this successful?

Where did things escalate?

What was that caused by?

What did you learn about yourself in the process?